Leisure Time CROSSWORDS™

VOLUME 6

Packed with Easy-to-Solve Crosswords™!

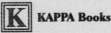

KAPPA Books

Visit us at www.kappapuzzles.com

CROSSWORD 1

Across

1. Mrs., in Mexico
4. Boxing outcomes (abbr.)
8. Chicken chow __
12. "Moby-Dick" captain
13. Crawl
14. Avoid
15. Snug rooms
16. "I __ Song Go Out of My Heart" (2 wds.)
17. Enrich
18. Archaeologist's outing
19. Bullring yell
20. Sony rival
22. Decade segments (abbr.)
23. Yarn bundle
25. Rabbit features
27. Log floats
31. Zoo attractions
34. Provides weapons
37. Owen Wilson's brother
39. Privileged few
41. Actress Benaderet
42. Bring together
44. Convent resident
45. __ Allan Poe
48. Therefore
49. G-men
50. Developers' interests
52. Hitchhiker's signal
54. Wharton grads
56. Smoking devices
60. Subway stop (abbr.)
63. Rescue worker (abbr.)
64. La Plata's locale (abbr.)
66. "__ Loser" (2 wds.)
67. Desert "taxi"
69. Uncomplicated
71. Gymnast's move
72. Imitative ones
73. Singer James
74. Degenerates
75. Affleck and Vereen
76. Reclined
77. "__ a boy!"

Down

1. 1921 Valentino film, with "The"
2. Kitchen appliance
3. Not in school (abbr.)
4. Money drawer
5. Leg bender
6. Fall mo.
7. Portion
8. Tues. preceder
9. Small whirlpool
10. Sikorsky or Stravinsky
11. Breaking stories
12. Finds sums
14. Sweetie-pie
19. Off __ tangent (2 wds.)
21. Ripken of Cooperstown
24. Federal tax agcy.
26. Scale note

28. Winter illness
29. Adjust
30. Woman's garment
32. Innings count, usually
33. Decorative nail
34. "Honest" President
35. Scarlet, ruby, etc.
36. Crèche figures
38. Quartet before I
40. Some Scrabble tiles
43. "__ Bet Your Life"
46. 24-hour teller (abbr.)
47. Insurgents
49. Hoover's gp.

51. U.S.A.'s "Uncle"
53. Fuel economy stat
55. Hard metal
57. Earhart, e.g.
58. Sends forth
59. Tree fluids
60. Non-union worker
61. Record
62. Prayer finale
64. __ spumante
65. Meg or Nolan
68. Speech pauses
70. __ snail's pace (2 wds.)
71. Weekday (abbr.)

CROSSWORD 2

Across

1. Q followers
4. Indigent
8. Remote
12. Monopoly pair
13. Carpool __
14. Cut bread
15. "__ Almighty"
16. Above
17. Columbus vessel
18. "Electric" swimmer
19. Pulver, e.g. (abbr.)
20. Before, in poems
22. Seer's gift (abbr.)
23. Nighttime fantasy
25. "King __"
27. Go over the books
31. Impostor
34. Korbut of gymnastics
37. Lennon or Wayne
39. Throat infection
41. Pro
42. More positive
44. Prankster's plot
45. Talent
48. Perform alone
49. Greek goddess
50. Mr. Doubleday
52. Sanctify
54. Fighter pilots
56. Revolutionary Allen
60. Family member
63. "Yuck!"
64. "This __ recording" (2 wds.)
66. "__ Blue?" (2 wds.)
67. Possessive pronoun
69. "__ girl!" (2 wds.)
71. Cosmetics company
72. Name on Shaq's uniform
73. Cuticle's spot
74. Gambling city
75. Ready for the rummage pile
76. Become submerged
77. Verb ending

Down

1. Rhone or Meuse
2. Dieter's device
3. Twice five
4. Architect's drawing
5. Munchies for Mr. Ed
6. Lennon's widow Yoko __
7. Drive back, as invaders
8. "The Greatest"
9. Library charge
10. Performs
11. Harvest
12. Homeowner's paper
14. Stalks of asparagus
19. Australian bird
21. Football flagger
24. Motorists' group (abbr.)
26. Barn pest
28. Record players (abbr.)
29. Debt markers
30. Pulsate
32. Impulse

33. Letter opening
34. Out of tune
35. Singer Falana
36. Yank
38. Singer Carter
40. Golf gp.
43. Caviar base
46. All __ day's work (2 wds.)
47. Make new ringlets
49. FDR's successor
51. Standard (abbr.)
53. Bounding main
55. Legs' fronts

57. Sanctuary
58. "__ My Souvenirs"
59. El __ (weather phenomenon)
60. Pack
61. Shout of dismay (2 wds.)
62. Poetic never
64. "Beauty __ the eye…" (2 wds.)
65. Jonas or Lee
68. 007 creator Fleming
70. Skater Babilonia
71. Tycoon Onassis

CROSSWORD 3

Across

1. Beach particles
5. Suffix for a doctrine
8. British fliers' gp.
11. Shoe stretchers
13. View
16. Freud's concern
17. Stroll
18. Karenina and Christie
19. Verb ending
20. Poker call (2 wds.)
22. Golden Gate and George Washington
24. Furious
26. What Marley wore in "Scrooge"
27. Passenger
28. "Hooked __ Feeling" (2 wds.)
31. Bring to a close
32. Frankenstein's helper
33. Eyes amorously
35. Dodgers' org.
38. Eye part
39. Pamper
40. Caboose's position
41. Mr. and __
42. Narrow valleys
43. Actress Martinelli
44. Island (Fr.)
45. Candied tuber

47. __ and found
48. Legislates a tax
51. Afr. animal
53. Reminder
54. Hamm and Farrow
55. DDE's military arena
56. Compact
58. Whither
62. FBI worker (abbr.)
63. Make fit
64. Some tides
65. Stubbed item
66. Deli loaf
67. Math problems

Down

1. RR stop
2. Sea inlet
3. Omaha's state (abbr.)
4. Hands over the mail
5. Lendl of tennis
6. Misdeed
7. CNN rival
8. Royal rule
9. De Mille of dance
10. Heavy mists
12. Half (prefix)
14. North Carolina native (2 wds.)
15. Chinese and Japanese people
21. Commitment phrase (2 wds.)
23. Achieved
24. Tavern request

25. Shackles
27. Digital camera's lack
29. Slangy denial
30. Great pain
34. Actress Kudrow
35. Gourd
36. Cowboy's rope
37. Insufferable child
39. Rained icily
40. Enjoys immensely
42. Billie's "Oz" character
44. "__ got it!"
46. Modern diagnostic tool (abbr.)
48. Unhand (2 wds.)
49. Be theatrical
50. Undersea detection device
52. Kate Hudson's mom Goldie
53. Butcher's product
54. Measure (out)
57. "I __" (Cosby series)
59. __ Claire, Wisconsin
60. Dashboard abbr.
61. Curvy letter

CROSSWORD 4

Across

1. Pounds (abbr.)
4. Furtive whisper
8. Siamese
12. Not in
13. Musical instrument
14. __ gold
15. Sis's sibling
16. Make payment
17. Flag pin site
18. Wears away gradually
20. "El __" (Marty Robbins hit)
22. Igloo material
23. Musical composition
24. Single-masted vessel
26. Elevator pioneer
29. Talked in a monotone
33. Winter ailment
36. Ellipses
39. Pastrami parlor
40. Place for mascara
42. Relent
44. "For goodness' __!"
45. Officer's staffer
46. Praises
48. Went on a pension (abbr.)
49. Actor Marlon
52. Merge
54. Closed auto
57. Make corrections
60. Gloomy
63. Nevada resort
64. Caron of "Gigi"
66. Sandwich leftover
68. Distinguishing quality
70. "...man __ mouse?" (2 wds.)
71. Narrow passageway
72. Actress Watson
73. Fido's doc
74. 1916 hit song
75. Old Dodge model
76. McMahon and others

Down

1. Earring place
2. Small donkey
3. Veranda
4. Dessert selections
5. Uncle __
6. Uses scissors
7. Add
8. Burnt __ crisp (2 wds.)
9. Western Indian
10. Actor Baldwin
11. Maui, e.g.
13. Magician's cry
14. Astound, informally
19. Batman and Robin, e.g.
21. Turf
25. Pea holders
27. Clinging vine
28. Boat canvas
30. Come close
31. Sommer of "The Prize"

32. Eating regimen
33. Toning target
34. Bear's home
35. Food inspection initials
37. Field
38. Run-down area
41. Biddies
43. Ike's initials
47. Like icy rain
50. Kentucky __ (race)
51. Poem of praise
53. Dentist's degree (abbr.)

55. Put a chip in the kitty
56. Actress Shearer
58. "P.S. __ You" (2 wds.)
59. Grew weary
60. Peruse
61. Woody Guthrie's son
62. Lacking interest
64. Bounciness
65. Breaks bread
67. "Cry __ River" (2 wds.)
69. Broadcast

CROSSWORD 5

Across

1. Baldwin of "The Departed"
5. Booty
9. Footnote abbr.
13. Company's symbol
14. Sulks
16. Stallion's date
17. Pea-soupers
18. Obvious
19. Miss a step
20. Blotched
22. Conceited one
24. Lend a hand
25. Sob
26. Heartless Romeo
29. Teacher's __
31. Shortened a skirt
35. Returned to earth
37. 2:1, e.g.
39. On a voyage
41. Author Philip ("Goodbye, Columbus")
42. Golf standard
43. Takes advantage of
44. Ford product
45. Doesn't give away
47. Singing bird
48. Window type
50. Envision
52. "You betcha!"
53. Switch settings
54. '30s relief agency (abbr.)
56. Secure
60. Make clear
64. "The __ King"
65. Explode
67. Harvest
69. Overflow
70. Unhand (2 wds.)
71. She (Fr.)
72. Heights (abbr.)
73. Phobia
74. Multitude

Down

1. Landon of politics
2. Hover
3. Waffle brand
4. __ Rica
5. Burn without flame
6. Made cloth
7. Imitated
8. Munich's land (abbr.)
9. "__ Excited" (2 wds.)
10. South Seas isle
11. Eye part
12. Store section (abbr.)
15. Dorm room fixture
21. Foul __
23. Personal trainer's workplace
25. Nest sounds
26. "Fame" singer Irene

27. Spoken
28. The same
30. Narrow candles
32. Manhandle
33. School composition
34. Tractor producer
36. Norse thunder god
38. Edison's initials
40. Makes inquiries
45. Shelter for dogs
46. Lawmaker
49. Miss Piggy's word for "me"

51. Stray
55. Buenos ___
56. Lingerie brand
57. Robin's beak
58. Tipster
59. Picnic invaders
60. Comely
61. Inits. for Lopez
62. Stumbled
63. Connecticut university
66. Ump's counterpart
68. Sunday bench

CROSSWORD 6

Across
1. Weight
5. Immense
8. Spill the beans
12. Sailing on the briny
13. Indian emblem
15. Shriek
16. Caution
17. "Laughing" animal
18. Icicle's spot
19. Bruce Lee's expertise (2 wds.)
21. It follows Sun.
22. Headless nail
23. "Oz" aunt et al.
25. Word after ship or Chips
27. Village green structure
30. Those in debt
33. Agreeable words
34. Defective car
37. French summer
39. Small (suffix)
40. Sharp, as color
41. Denote
42. It follows Mon.
43. Broaden
44. Manicurist of commercials
45. Clean one's feathers
47. __ longue (garden chair)

49. Vigoda and Burrows
51. Comic strip scream
52. "Oh, woe!"
55. Gloomy guy
57. Experience again
62. Short note
63. All kidding __
65. Ripened
66. Spoken
67. Moreno et al.
68. __ John Silver
69. Creates lace
70. Double curve
71. Comic Johnson

Down
1. Dove's opposite
2. Jacob's twin
3. Feathery plant
4. Zesty taste
5. Part of BSA
6. Line-__ veto
7. Italian seaport
8. "__ Birdie" (2 wds.)
9. TV producer Norman
10. Edison's middle name
11. Ran, as dye
13. Mitten part
14. Masculinity
20. Legal charges
24. Hard
26. Hold one's __
27. Arise (2 wds.)
28. Fall flower

29. Twenty-sixth letter
31. Swamp grasses
32. Actor's platform
33. In addition
35. Eden female
36. Dice
38. WSW's opp.
40. Salad dressing ingredient
41. __ tai
43. Spider's handiwork
44. Design
46. Artists' stands
48. "__ Johnny!"
50. "Q" of song
52. Loads (2 wds.)
53. Former currency in Florence
54. College course (abbr.)
56. Poses
58. "Ooh-__" (hyph.)
59. Dr. Frankenstein's helper
60. Release anger
61. Favorable margin
64. Prosecutors (abbr.)

CROSSWORD 7

Across

1. Rustic hotels
5. Mirth
9. German car inits.
12. Somewhat cold
13. Graduates
15. Shoe width
16. "Star Wars" creature
17. Famed tenor Enrico __
18. Test tube's home, for short
19. NBC, e.g.
21. Barriers
23. Greek god
24. Aykroyd of "Soul Man"
25. Hold office
29. "Halt" crier
32. Fake name
33. Ten-cent coins
35. One lacking grace
37. Catcher's glove
38. Reverent
39. Bundle
40. One Gabor
41. "Sing __ with Mitch"
42. Actress Dressler
43. Writer Glyn
45. Tasty tidbit
46. Beatty of "Superman"
47. Fragment
49. Muslim faith
52. Removing suds
56. King (Fr.)
57. Consumption
60. Sweet and __ chicken
62. It preceded the CIA
63. Respond
64. Moreover
65. Crooner "King" Cole
66. Actress Tuesday
67. Bulb measure

Down

1. Like some roads in winter
2. Midday
3. Stem part
4. Blind strip
5. Stare
6. Lies in wait
7. Grounded Aussie bird
8. Pennsylvania has three
9. Ringing device
10. Supper, for one
11. Spiders' homes
13. Squash type
14. Ames natives
20. Clashes
22. Colony insect
24. They're worse than cees
25. Amusement
26. Pimiento holder
27. Essential
28. Have a snack

29. Complacent
30. Lions' sounds
31. Connecticut Ivy Leaguer
33. Couturier Christian
34. Charged atom
36. Experience
38. Walk heavily
39. Tavern
41. Blood condition
42. Cleans up a puddle
44. __ jam (2 wds.)
45. Pit worker
47. Move on hands and knees
48. Tramped
49. Wrinkle flattener
50. Home run hitter Sammy
51. Catalog
53. "__ Mommy Kissing Santa Claus" (2 wds.)
54. Lopez's theme
55. Blast of wind
58. Opp. of SSE
59. Mao __-tung
61. Decompose

CROSSWORD 8

Across

1. Wonderful, slangily
4. It follows morning (abbr.)
7. Coagulate
10. Andrews, for one (abbr.)
13. "Notes __ Scandal" (2006 film, 2 wds.)
14. Fawn's mom
15. Mature
16. Tell tall tales
17. NJ's ocean
18. Comic DeLuise
19. Sports fan's jeer
20. Gave permission
21. Large bean
23. Records (abbr.)
25. Closes tightly
27. Traditions
31. "The __ Griffith Show"
32. Bite down hard
35. Chops into cubes
37. Luncheonette patrons
39. Nonprofessional
42. Doggy bag morsel
43. Halloween mo.
45. "Murder, __"
46. Rested
48. Went by car
51. Tangible objects
53. Fixed look
54. Wipe away a mistake
55. Alan of "M*A*S*H"
58. Artist Pablo
61. Jungle sounds
63. Korean auto company
64. "People who __ people..."
68. Suffix for a doctrine
69. Hurricane's center
72. Bomb
74. Pub offering
75. Visualize
76. Convened
77. Ike's theater
78. Brink
79. Lisper's problem letter
80. "The Lady __ Tramp" (2 wds.)
81. __ Moines
82. New (prefix)

Down

1. Its mama's a mare
2. Against (prefix)
3. Healing ointment
4. Find a sum
5. Simpletons
6. Lure
7. Chat
8. Conceit
9. Gorcey and Carroll
10. Poe's middle name
11. Take, as a question
12. Seamstress Ross
22. Pinnacle
24. Carbonated drink
26. Soften
28. Remove forcibly
29. Puccini heroine
30. Meager

32. Company's head (abbr.)
33. Mar
34. Broadway lyricist Harbach
36. Engraves
38. Throw out
40. Annapolis school (abbr.)
41. Waste cloths
44. Actress Garr
47. Half a fly
49. Peter the Great, for one
50. Ship's floor

52. Tough metal
55. Leave bed
56. Suffers defeat
57. Women of rank
59. Assisted
60. Fry lightly
62. Tractor-trailer
65. Receive wages
66. "Night" author Wiesel
67. Car dealer's model
70. "Certainly!"
71. Airport monitor abbr.
73. Roberto's "two"

CROSSWORD 9

Across

1. Representative (abbr.)
4. Football shoe's gripper
9. Sardine containers
13. Cat noise
15. __ Janeiro (2 wds.)
16. Data, informally
17. Author Wiesel
18. __ beauty
19. Germinated grain
20. Concentrates
22. __ tai
24. "SportsCenter" channel
25. More considerate
28. Habitation
31. __ Fe
33. Actor Ayres
35. Eats at the Ritz
36. Prescribed food
37. Personality
38. Grew old
39. __ down (note)
40. Declare firmly
41. NYC transit org.
42. Epps or Sharif
44. Golf tournaments
45. Fa's follower
46. Cher's ex
48. Three-card __
49. Biblical hymns

51. Sale condition (2 wds.)
53. Edgar Allan __
54. Fly-hitting gadget
57. Practice boxing
60. Things, e.g.
62. Asian country
64. Half (prefix)
65. Stories
66. Estrada of "CHiPs"
67. Frozen rain
68. Den
69. Paper layer

Down

1. Orangutan, e.g.
2. The __ of Mexico
3. The Dixie Chicks, e.g.
4. Apple __ (dessert)
5. Bedding
6. Very long time periods
7. Citrus beverage
8. White ant
9. Like a rabbit
10. "Away __ Manger" (2 wds.)
11. League for the Cowboys (abbr.)
12. Drunkard
14. Ebbed
21. Manipulates
23. Med. school subj.
25. Make socks
26. "Ocean's __"

27. Ruler
28. Second president
29. Circus tent (2 wds.)
30. Shaq and Ryan
32. Beautify
34. More unpleasant
39. Murray and Peerce
40. Disciple
42. Nordic capital
43. Seconds
44. Overlook
47. Acted bored
50. Rainy month

52. Impudent
54. "Star Trek" helmsman
55. Western lawman Wyatt
56. Irritate
57. Moviegoer's admonition
58. Tiny vegetable
59. French friend
61. Cheerios grain
63. Star's home

CROSSWORD 10

Across

1. "Is __ so?"
5. Raring to go
9. Hair mousse, e.g.
13. Wife of Zeus
14. Bound
15. Verb form
16. Author Bagnold
17. Take __ the lam (2 wds.)
18. Touches on
19. Cold cubes
20. Archie Bunker's wife
22. Rudy, to Theo Huxtable
23. Take back
27. Cripple
29. Yoko __
30. Clown props
34. Mix in a confused way
39. Concepts
40. Ollie's pal
41. Critic Roger
43. Rave's partner
44. Flashlight, in England
46. Visual detection
48. Weed out
50. Blockhead
51. Light __
53. Riding the waves
57. Large ocean (abbr.)
60. Sparse
62. Likewise not
63. Put a sari on
65. Golf gadgets
67. Napoleon's exile isle
68. Exec's notes
69. Elvis shook them
70. Women, informally
71. Slant
72. "Born Free" lioness
73. Has to pay

Down

1. That group's
2. Therefore
3. One with an April 12 birthday
4. Lincoln's son
5. Larter of "Heroes"
6. Cast a ballot
7. MP3 player from Apple
8. Overalls material
9. Shortest mo.
10. Responsibility
11. __ spumante
12. Navy chow
15. Pacific paradise
21. British thanks
24. Type of pipe
25. __ tizzy (2 wds.)
26. Alaskan city
28. Battle of the bulge locale
31. Thin
32. Astronauts' OJ

33. Grounded jet (abbr.)
34. Road sign
35. Author John Dickson __
36. Air-rifle ammo
37. Maui garland
38. Energy unit
40. R-V connection
42. "__ Swell"
45. Residences
47. Do roadwork
49. Doter's treatment (abbr.)
52. Soak in the tub

53. Dance movements
54. Mother-__ (hyph.)
55. Like an earl or a count
56. Mower's target
57. Naval chiefs (abbr.)
58. "Star __"
59. Uncool, slangily
61. Singer Diamond
64. Comic strip "socko!"
66. Retirement benefit agcy.
67. Self-concept

CROSSWORD 11

Across
1. Ship's letters
4. Grounded jets (abbr.)
8. Sink or __
12. Thick rug
14. Blender setting
16. Corn dish
17. Eat
18. Employing
19. Jot
20. Mime
21. "__ Rita"
22. Actor Gale
24. Parcel (out)
26. "__ Karenina"
27. Shadowboxes
29. Hearty beef dish
33. Jaworski and Spinks
34. Jukebox selections
36. Chinese chairman
37. Some paints
38. Swelling reducer
39. Taskmaster
40. Alias letters
41. Ladies and __
43. Hair salon action
44. Navy town in Virginia
46. Like London's weather, often
47. Certain debts
48. Cut open
49. Go up
52. "Strangers __ Train" (2 wds.)
53. Facts, informally
57. Farm structure
58. Poe's first name
60. "Count __!" (2 wds.)
61. Actor Pitt
62. Mournful melody
63. Kitchen follower
64. Farm animals
65. Disarrange
66. Govt. agcy.

Down
1. Govt. food-regulating agcy.
2. Seagoing vessel
3. Of sound mind
4. Gushes
5. "If You Knew __"
6. Three singers
7. Lawmaker (abbr.)
8. Corkscrew
9. Actress Natalie
10. Involved with
11. Imply
13. Berlin natives
15. Christmas beverage
23. Burden
25. Sounds of hesitation
26. Actress Moorehead

27. Watchmaker
28. "The __ Express"
30. In the midst of
31. Apt to talk back
32. Lawn sprinkler
33. Banker's specialty
34. Basins
35. Pumpkin-carving mo.
39. Vaudevillian's ambition (2 wds.)
41. Thug
42. Avoided adroitly

43. King, in Paris
45. Little devils
46. Highway signals
48. Hidden obstacles
49. Etc., e.g.
50. Lee of baked goods
51. Study furiously
52. Dreadful monster
54. Snoods
55. Tantrums
56. Draft status (hyph.)
59. Like romantic lighting

CROSSWORD 12

Across

1. House addition
4. Figured (out)
9. Speed abbr.
12. Neckwear
14. Got around
16. Width of Shaq's shoes
17. Applaud
18. Annoy
19. Hebrew high priest
20. Gear in a '50s bachelor pad (hyph.)
21. Artist Yoko
22. Water mammal
24. Decays
26. Overcome difficulties
28. Washbowls
31. Perch at the opera (2 wds.)
34. Make jubilant
35. Chop up
36. Gracefully slight
38. Tippler
39. Jailed one
40. Mrs. Eddie Cantor
41. Comparative word
43. Tra-__ (hyph.)
44. Of the moon
46. Zoologist's subjects
48. Dromedaries
49. Ensuing
50. "Andy __"
51. Fairy tale monsters
54. Winter malady
55. Ancient Peruvian
59. French island
60. Parisian farewells
63. Gather grain
64. Hawaii airport giveaway
65. __ seed
66. Roof overhang
67. Longing
68. Complains
69. Spearheaded

Down

1. Engrave initials
2. "Hi __, Hi Lo"
3. Turn pages
4. Transportation terminals
5. Baking compartments
6. El __, Texas
7. New York time (abbr.)
8. "Gidget" actress Sandra
9. Congregate
10. Brazilian soccer great
11. Inheritor
13. Courage
15. Rain bits
23. Golfers' gadgets
25. Unified
26. Ski lodge beverage

27. Conestoga wagon pullers
28. ___ in show
29. Honolulu greeting
30. Lucifer
31. Debtors' mail
32. Skirt style (hyph.)
33. ___ wave
35. Distributed cards
37. Snickers maker
39. Linen plant
42. Work start, for some
44. Santa's "seat"
45. Referee's kin
47. Plateaus
48. Makes happen
50. Tuft
51. Greasy
52. Merriment
53. Horse strap
54. Dread
56. Actress Patricia
57. Mountain hideout
58. Was imitative
61. It follows Nov.
62. "This ___ recording" (2 wds.)

CROSSWORD 13

Across

1. Teen's channel choice (abbr.)
4. Sailboat part
8. Long cut
12. Author Wister
14. Complies
16. "Have a __ day!"
17. Entertainer Moreno
18. Princess's headgear
19. Hot place
20. Drawer pull
21. Ferber et al.
22. Comedian Foxx
23. Runs in neutral
25. Laughing sound
27. One of the Alous
29. Is disloyal
33. Impart knowledge
34. Improper
36. Be sorry
37. Courageous one
38. It has 30 teams (abbr.)
39. Elbow action
40. Great skill
41. Secluded spots
43. Knight's shining suit
44. Everyman's tops (hyph.)
46. Pacific __
47. Football cheer
48. Rents
50. Greek sandwich
53. Rewrite
55. Refs' kin
59. Amount borrowed
60. Esther of "Good Times"
61. Protective ditch
62. Garfield's friend
63. Of the sun
64. Green with __
65. Like Kojak
66. Mama pigs
67. Cowboy Ritter

Down

1. "__ & Mindy"
2. Castor, to Pollux
3. President's "no"
4. Tourists' stopovers
5. Observe, as laws
6. Connery and Penn
7. Supermodel Banks
8. Loud sleeper
9. Not taped
10. Decorated a cake
11. Wait on
13. Cookie brand
15. Cummerbunds
24. Teen's retort
26. Aliens (abbr.)

27. Mocks
28. Dirt
29. Babies' protectors
30. Fragrance
31. Canadian territory
32. Medium
33. Definite thing
34. Bible book
35. Civil rights leader's monogram
39. Take for granted
41. Gun lobby (abbr.)
42. Additional people

43. Sleeve card
45. Pressed clothes
46. Military instructions
48. "__, Dolly!"
49. Jeb Bush, to Laura (hyph.)
50. Lump
51. "Star Wars" creature
52. Hobo transportation
54. Cattle calls
56. __ Blanc
57. Do roadwork
58. Mythical river

CROSSWORD 14

Across

1. College student
5. Equal
9. Eight, to Eduardo
13. Cutlass
15. Lo-cal word
16. Bundle up
17. Sharpshooter Oakley
18. Mr. Griffin
19. Garage job, for short
20. "The __ Side"
22. Juncture
24. Opposite of max.
25. Illegal liquor
29. Be disbelieving
31. Certain PCs
32. Politician Landon
34. Fireplace residue
35. Teacher's group (abbr.)
36. Entertainer Falana
38. Flambeau
42. Ethnic fast food order
44. Perhaps
46. Laugh sounds (2 wds.)
47. School assignment
49. Blab
50. Mover's truck
51. Possessed
53. Clergy mem.
54. Brazilian soccer legend
55. Sky color

57. Comments
59. Common contraction
60. Vampire's target
63. Drunkard
64. Pause
66. Early computer game
68. Green fruits
72. Johnson of "Laugh-In"
73. Robert __ (2 wds.)
74. Greene of "Bonanza"
75. Mythical river to the underworld
76. Want
77. Faction

Down

1. R.E. Lee's gp.
2. __ up to (admit)
3. Long time period
4. Floats
5. Common street name
6. Competes
7. To be (Fr.)
8. The Silver State
9. Nocturnal bird
10. Smidgen of bread
11. Nun's outfit
12. Milk carton instruction
14. "Let's Make a __"
21. Royal domain
23. Greatest portion
25. Spree
26. Minds orders
27. Bradley et al.

28. Boast
30. "Trouble's coming!" (hyph.)
33. Philadelphia hockey player
37. More skilled
39. Irrational talker
40. Tailor's marker
41. Underwear name
43. Honolulu's island
45. Sprites
48. Tall tale
52. Intensify
54. Courtyards
55. Stave off

56. Tangy
58. Richard of "Night Court"
59. Some nest eggs (abbr.)
61. Singer Nat "King" __
62. Reflex-checking spot
65. John Ritter's dad
67. Diploma alternative (abbr.)
69. Modern diagnostic test (abbr.)
70. Conclusion
71. Comprehend

CROSSWORD 15

Across

1. Home
6. Macho toiletry label
10. Leo the Lion's movie studio
13. Infants
14. Reckless
15. Ponder
16. Marital joy
17. "__ of Green Gables"
18. Trouble the waters
19. Sasquatch's cousin
20. From Milan (abbr.)
21. "__ It Romantic?"
22. Gala dress
25. Dug for silver
27. Old Testament book
29. Gregorian __
31. Chaney of films
32. Penalized
34. Transferable picture
38. Wintertime truck attachment
40. Sheds feathers
42. Test-driver's car
43. __ steak
45. Crowbar, for one
47. Whether or __
48. Young pigeon
50. Prices
52. Water pitchers
54. Proofreading notation
55. Sir's companion
56. Vaulted doorway
59. Filmdom's Preminger
63. Amorous glance
64. Belle's boyfriend
65. Lawn cutter
66. "I've __ thinking…"
67. Endure
68. Getting older
69. Fourth-year students (abbr.)
70. Caribous' kin
71. Divides

Down

1. Dalton of "Falcon Crest"
2. Large bundle
3. Sad notice, for short
4. Pattern
5. Pluralizing letter
6. Skull contents
7. Speak wildly
8. Annapolis inst.
9. "__ & Louise"
10. Elk's cousin
11. Prepare coffee beans
12. Dissolve
15. Produced on a press
23. Dunderhead
24. Spur-of-the-moment mood
26. Not Rep. or Dem.
27. Shock
28. __ about

(approximately, 2 wds.)

29. Autograph hound's prey, for short
30. 21st-century electronics advance (abbr.)
31. Vinyl records (abbr.)
33. Lopez's theme song
35. Copper coin
36. Singer Tori
37. Land parcel
39. Magi (2 wds.)
41. Religious group
44. Alphabetic trio
46. Shad __
49. Serviceable
51. Patsy
52. Zealous
53. England's neighbor
54. Closes
55. Unruly groups
57. The __ McCoy
58. Keg
60. Jenna, to Barbara
61. Mind
62. Professional gps.
65. Blemish

CROSSWORD 16

Across

1. Tuna __
5. __ Andreas fault
8. Fine dress material
12. Locales
14. Fatigue
16. Threesome
17. Skater Henie
18. Cheese from Holland
19. Play boisterously
20. Truman's monogram
21. Canadian Indian
23. Calls long-distance
25. Boat
26. Failed to be honest
27. Propped up tomatoes
30. Take into custody
33. Tax return reviews
34. Three-__ sloth
35. Advanced degree (abbr.)
37. Trudge
38. Air-rifle ammo
39. "Dumb __" of the comics
40. Bro, to sis
41. Greenish blue
43. Food store proprietor
45. Elephant's treat
47. Tennis __
48. Agitated state
49. Weasel's silky cousin
50. Decrease
53. Bell sound
54. LP abbr.
57. Rights group (abbr.)
58. Wind
60. "__ Gay" (plane)
62. Sudden urge
63. Knitter's material
64. Type of auto
65. Negative reply
66. Lawyer's charge
67. Franklin and Jonson

Down

1. Pummel potatoes
2. Love god
3. Pre-Easter period
4. __ Mahal
5. Brew tea
6. General's assistant
7. Heston's gp.
8. Walked with confidence
9. Golf club
10. Cocktail garnish
11. Keystone __
13. Drawer freshener
15. "The __ Strikes Back"
22. Exterminates
24. Company of cows
25. Sideslip
26. Asian land

27. Weakens
28. Bulb flower
29. Southwestern brick
31. "Star Trek" Vulcan
32. Trio's number
34. Vague schedule info (abbr.)
36. Run suddenly
38. Ram into
39. Wharf
41. History's Boleyn
42. Music producer Jones
43. Jumbo smile

44. Stoves
46. Take for granted
49. He created Eeyore
50. Plastic flamingo's place
51. Canyon feedback
52. Lingerie item
53. Awful
54. Took taxis
55. Look ahead
56. Provides workers
59. Simpleton
61. Dick Cavett's home st.

CROSSWORD 17

Across

1. Cape Cod's ocean (abbr.)
4. Type of car
8. Deceive
12. Tobacco unit
14. Cartoon chipmunk
16. Caesar's "and others" (2 wds.)
17. Stylist's focus
18. "Observe!"
19. Pitcher's illegal motion
20. To be (Fr.)
21. Not Dem. or Rep.
22. Lullaby composer Johannes
24. Sink problem
26. Lincoln and Vigoda
27. Chemist's vessel
30. Lucky dice rolls
33. Goes by bus
34. Actress Beryl
36. Stout's cousin
38. Smells
39. Actor Byrnes
40. Snooped
42. Spider's domain
43. Assess
44. Black bird
45. Took five

48. Capital of Kansas
49. Touches gently
50. Ostentation
51. Merciful
54. "__ Abner"
55. Building extensions
59. Preowned
60. Figure
62. Disturb
63. Actress Falco
64. Laid a bathroom floor
65. Slipcover location
66. Hourglass filler
67. Source of poi
68. __ Hampshire

Down

1. Tooth trouble
2. Not this
3. Lion's abode
4. Messiah
5. Accompanying
6. Craving eagerly
7. Cartoonist Keane
8. Lower
9. Mormon state
10. __ Beach, Florida
11. BPOE members
13. Tow truck
15. Caught
23. Race an engine
25. Not as much
26. Put __ (shelve)

27. Forehead
28. Down source
29. Sun-dried brick
31. Artless
32. Like a panther
34. Studies
35. NYC summer setting
37. Writer Ferber
40. School dance
41. Ice-T, Ice Cube, and Vanilla Ice
43. Makeup exam
46. Turned over earth

47. Sunbathe
48. Ohio city
50. Bagpipe player
51. Tints
52. Food inspection initials
53. Shrimp lo __
54. Tra followers (hyph.)
56. Water bird
57. "__ with Father"
58. Cabbage dish
61. Broadway success

CROSSWORD 18

Across

1. Drivers license issuers (abbr.)
4. Float gently
8. Command to a dog
11. Hawaiian island
12. Violin's big brother
13. Merely
15. Female voice
16. Bye, in Buenos Aires
17. Frame of mind
18. Place for shadow
20. Defers a prison sentence
22. South Bend's state (abbr.)
23. Halloween handout
24. Erasable writing tool
27. Pie serving
30. "__ aboard!"
31. Listened
34. Mona Lisa's feature
36. Ballot
38. Stainers
40. For always
41. Particles
43. Carpet ruiners
45. "__ had it!"
46. Show disdain
48. In a __ (in trouble)
50. Extend
53. Sped
54. Preface
57. Turn to ice
61. Whimper
62. Less decorated
64. Midterm, e.g.
65. Throw off
66. Sardonic wit
67. Kisser's target
68. Last-yr. students
69. Caroled
70. Holy men (abbr.)

Down

1. Tyne of "Cagney & Lacey"
2. Like Harpo
3. Stradivarius
4. Said "I do"
5. Tilting, at sea
6. Cake ingredient
7. Flips
8. At any date in the future
9. Sharing a secret (2 wds.)
10. Oaf
11. Actress West
12. Carried golf clubs
14. Football measures (abbr.)
19. 1/12 foot
21. Companions
24. Conspiracies
25. Music legend John

26. Deposits
28. Courteous
29. French student
30. Gardner of films
32. GOP mem.
33. Sign of rain
35. Sooner than, in poetry
37. Green gems
39. Utilize a wok (hyph.)
42. Appear
44. Battle reminder
47. Hebrew clergymen

49. Prepares to propose
51. Nurse Barton
52. Egret
54. Public TV letters
55. Fans' shouts
56. Water jug
58. Passage out
59. Microwaves, informally
60. "Oz" aunt and others
63. Liverpool's locale (abbr.)

CROSSWORD 19

Across

1. TV network
4. Feels sick
8. "Back in the ___" (Beatles)
12. Bungle
14. "Peter Pan" pirate
15. Paper unit
17. Band instrument
18. Considerate
19. Actor Sal
20. Become embarrassed
22. Topped with ice cream (3 wds.)
24. Misjudge
25. Snow runner
26. ___ Fields cookies
27. Muppet Miss
30. Go by
32. Cassini of fashion
33. Eddie of vaudeville
34. Sculpture pieces
38. ID digits
39. Harry Potter's pal
40. GI's bed
41. Gorilla, e.g.
42. Millinery case
44. Novelist Fleming
45. Flutter
46. Phonograph inventor
48. Buildings' locations
49. West of Hollywood
51. ___ de cologne
52. Celestial body
53. Hair curlers
55. Tankards' cousins
58. Duck
59. Tresses
61. Fido's wagger
63. Beauty shop rinse
64. Qualified
65. Word on a waffle box
66. Give the impression
67. Dog's sound
68. Reserved

Down

1. Sternward
2. Make unclear
3. Rubik's ___
4. Questioner
5. Poker phrase (2 wds.)
6. Actor Cariou
7. Songwriter Neil
8. Sch. for officers
9. Glisten
10. Spanish gentleman
11. Pastoral pipes
13. Bratty kid, e.g. (2 wds.)
16. Ballerina's ___ shoes
21. Waterless
23. Tetley competitor
25. Underhanded
27. Elegant

28. "Casablanca" heroine
29. Fellow
30. Very long time
31. Tippler
33. Craftier
35. Pretzel sprinkling
36. Mayberry lad
37. Stage designs
39. Fishing gear
40. Food container
43. Direct route
44. Promissory note
45. Having limits

47. Glide
48. "Sweet __" (song)
49. Chess maneuvers
50. Without company
52. __ throat
53. Fan's cry
54. Red-coated cheese
55. Window ledge
56. Complains
57. __ of relief
60. Honest nickname
62. Myrna of "Libeled Lady"

CROSSWORD 20

Across

1. Neighbor of Mich.
5. Sluggers' successes (abbr.)
9. Hee-hawer on the farm
12. __ of office
13. Dobbin's comment
14. Blemish
15. Deep __ bend
16. "__ of Two Cities" (2 wds.)
17. "M*A*S*H" star
18. Lean eater Jack
20. Fa follower
21. Shopper's item
22. "Nope" (hyph.)
24. Common face shape
26. Actress Eden
29. Legislates
33. Irving and Carter
34. Tel __
37. Revere
38. Head's "yes"
39. Nearest
41. Action star Diesel
42. Actress Garbo
44. Complain
45. Subjects of society news
46. Venus's sister
48. Candidate
50. Guns the motor
52. __ out

53. Move slightly
56. Parisian pal
58. Before beta
61. "Say it isn't so!" (2 wds.)
62. Giant
64. Regulations
66. Will beneficiary
67. Make amends
68. Sunburn-healing plant
69. Canadian prov.
70. Housing payment
71. Shrill bark

Down

1. Chinese skillet
2. Hunter and Holm
3. "__ lively!"
4. Chubby-cheeked children
5. On a pension (abbr.)
6. Partiality
7. Snow abode
8. Put aside
9. For __ care (2 wds.)
10. Lays pre-grown grass
11. Doctor's word for "quick"
13. Without affectations
14. Romantic song
19. "By Jove!"
23. Chaos
25. Medical school subj.
26. Knocks loudly

(supplements)

27. Love, Italian-style
28. Winona of "Dracula"
30. Witches' group
31. Hopi, for one
32. Feel
35. "The Lady ___ Tramp" (2 wds.)
36. French author Jules
39. Candy ___
40. Home to Gonzaga University
43. Fright
45. Exhibit
47. Visual online persona
49. Tormé or Brooks
51. Strike, OT-style
53. District in London
54. After that
55. First (abbr.)
57. Lay ___ the line (2 wds.)
59. Very fit
60. Army deserter (abbr.)
63. Picnic nuisance
65. Between Aug. and Oct.

CROSSWORD 21

Across

1. Artist Kahlo
6. Librarian's admonition
9. Cultivating implement
13. Spring bird
14. Sign of sorrow
16. Stride easily
17. Imitating
18. Yearning
19. Got older
20. Actor Danson
21. Author Ferber
23. Church laws
25. Skirt opening
26. Retail transaction
27. Revised copy
30. Jewelry fasteners
33. Heredity elements
34. Diamond and Sedaka
36. Type of roast
38. Chew upon
39. Shoemaker's helper
40. Ripped
41. Serious wrong
42. Tan
44. Imitated
45. Published diary
47. __ rod
48. City dwellings (abbr.)
49. Srta.'s neighbor
50. Strong craving
53. Cruise
54. Hero sandwich
57. Rock's partner
58. Sports cable network
60. Wipe clean
62. "__ Tired" (2 wds.)
63. Authentic
64. Spoken for
65. Nasty
66. Ironically humorous
67. Loses fur

Down

1. Univ. club
2. Double Dutch need
3. Footnote abbr.
4. Bothersome noise
5. Los __
6. Feat
7. Olympus queen
8. Witch
9. Jets
10. Company's symbol
11. Unroll
12. Gets married
15. Remember
22. Accomplished
24. Melodramatic cry
25. Slow-cooked dish
26. Asimov's realm (hyph.)

27. Bacon and __

28. Jeans material

29. Ridiculous

31. Product plug

32. Alarm

34. Gets closer

35. Forest animal

37. Garden plots

40. Poop out

42. Keystone figures

43. Baseball batter

44. Wooden hammers

46. A Wayans brother

47. Frazier's rival

49. Virile

50. Pare

51. Living quarters

52. Ingrid's role in "Casablanca"

53. Stout pole

54. "For Pete's __!"

55. Preowned

56. Gazzara and Vereen

59. Make homemade clothes

61. College cheer

CROSSWORD 22

Across

1. Recede
4. Glided
8. Aromatic spice
12. Blue
14. __ Boothe Luce
15. Farrow et al.
16. Type of dancer (hyph.)
17. Place of refuge
18. At rest
19. Antiquated
21. Pickpocket, e.g.
23. Ionian and Ross
24. Dogpatch's Daisy __
25. Actress Meryl
28. It spews lava
32. Discoverer's cry
33. Big rigs
35. Robert or Calvin
37. Spunky fortitude
39. Scruffs
41. Singer Guthrie
42. Singer Kate __
44. Put back to zero
46. Doggie doc
47. M'lady's bedroom
49. Withdraw
51. Melodic syllable
52. Clairvoyant one
53. __ of absence
56. Banners
60. Seed holders
61. Tour leader
63. Encounter
64. Cato's "therefore"
65. Playful swimmer
66. Ancestor
67. Shoreline hazard
68. At hand
69. Fleur-de-__

Down

1. Waffle brand
2. B-movie monster
3. Irks
4. Thin boards
5. Bathe
6. Intense rage
7. Pertaining to teeth
8. 2002, to Brutus
9. Executive staffer
10. Cow's offspring
11. Compass pt.
13. Bullwinkle J. __
14. Depreciate
20. Grant and Remick
22. Mild cussword
24. Hebrew lawgiver
25. Withers
26. Index finger's neighbor
27. Math proportion

28. Poisonous snake
29. __ king (2 wds.)
30. Sensitive spot
31. Lubricated
34. Newswoman Shriver
36. Brief comment
38. VWX preceders
40. More placid
43. Digital broadcasting system (abbr.)
45. Numeral suffix
48. California's neighbor
50. Studies hard

52. Passover meal
53. Folk knowledge
54. Outer limit
55. __ this date (now, 2 wds.)
56. Falafel's bread
57. __ Patrick Harris
58. Actress Hatcher
59. Fr. canonized women
60. Word in MPH
62. Southwestern Indian

CROSSWORD 23

Across

1. Pierre's friend
4. "Stop, Dobbin!"
8. Caresses gently
12. Some August babies
14. Burns
15. Very wicked
16. Gasp
17. Musical cadences
18. One Columbus ship
19. Thieves
21. Sir's counterpart
22. ___ the line (obeyed the rules)
23. Lass
25. ___ and smell the coffee (2 wds.)
28. Canadian province
32. Alda of "The Aviator"
33. Long-legged bird
35. Play area
36. Neither's partner
37. Pilfer
38. Comic Caesar
39. Penn's pronoun
41. Esau's twin
43. Ocean flow
44. Reuben, e.g.
46. Elevated
48. Minimum ___
49. "Animal House" costume
50. Detection device
53. Way to get around Disney World
57. ___ about (approximately, 2 wds.)
58. CIA employee
60. In addition
61. Pinochle term
62. Suri's mommy
63. Slide on ice
64. Cobblers' tools
65. A Baldwin brother
66. Those holding office

Down

1. Heidi's mountains
2. Beef
3. Actress Skye
4. Eerie
5. Holbrook and Linden
6. Table scrap
7. Domestic donkey
8. Hockey punishment
9. Ardent
10. Actress Louise
11. Bang shut
13. ___ Island, NY
14. Takes a nap
20. Gymnast Mary ___ Retton
21. Modern diagnostic tool (abbr.)
23. Actress Greta ___
24. Pen filler
25. Wishes
26. Oahu greeting

27. "Will & Grace" character
28. Sponge off of others
29. Desert stopover
30. Woman in white
31. Summed up
34. Use a stencil
40. Director Blake __
41. Lively dance
42. Anne, Charlotte, or Emily
43. Coronets
45. Civil, for one

47. Part of history
49. Bracer
50. Actress Downey
51. Again
52. Kewpie __
53. Dole (out)
54. "__ Know" (2 wds.)
55. The fat __ the fire (2 wds.)
56. Cuts off
58. Wanted poster inits.
59. Woman, informally

CROSSWORD 24

Across

1. Hertz's competitor
5. Advanced business deg.
8. "Arrivederci, __"
12. Rich Little, for one
14. Baseball great Berra
16. Divorced mates
17. Glimmer
18. Actor O'Neal
19. Weirdo
20. "__ in Black" (film)
21. Boat paddles
23. Smells awful
25. __ school
26. District in London
27. Orb
30. Appointment log
34. They open doors
35. Dry, as bread
37. Father
38. Adherent (suffix)
39. Great anger
40. Cool __ cucumber (2 wds.)
41. Supplies with a crew
43. Steering devices
45. __ about (approximately, 2 wds.)
46. Tablelands
48. DeGeneres and Burstyn
50. Invitation inits.
51. Land document
52. Camry maker
55. Actress Witherspoon
56. Jacuzzi spot
59. Iridescent gem
60. Actress Carter
62. Praline nut
64. Make known
65. Med. sch. course
66. Vowed
67. Lyric verses
68. Letters after a dentist's name
69. Ending for major

Down

1. Type of radio (hyph.)
2. Contemptible
3. "__ Ordinary Man" (2 wds.)
4. Bro's sibling
5. Magi gift
6. The Beach __
7. Turkish title
8. Districts
9. Work animals
10. Gentle
11. Invites
13. Singing group
15. Dr. Scholl's item
22. Has another birthday
24. "At __ Hop"
25. "__ So Fine"
26. Witch-hunting city

Across

27. Be stinting
28. Flower feature
29. "Laughing" creature
30. Hubbel and Sagan
31. Actress Ladd
32. Fiery felony
33. Raises, as children
36. Traffic snarl (hyph.)
42. Saunters
43. Cuban capital
44. Observer
45. Antique
47. Guess at a price (abbr.)
49. Bounds
51. Dunces
52. Dorothy's pet
53. Page for viewpoints (hyph.)
54. Cheney's alma mater
55. Clothed
56. Tartan wearer
57. Segment
58. Prince Charles's sister
61. Conclude
63. Woolly mama

CROSSWORD 25

Across
1. Hurt
5. It was, poetically
9. Sharif who played Zhivago
13. Italian wine town
14. Midwest airport
15. Rug nap
16. Fishing spot
17. Surrendered
18. Served perfectly
19. Roberto's friend
21. Authorizes
23. British composer Thomas
25. Alias initials
26. Endurance
29. __ Ocean
34. Departure's opposite (abbr.)
35. Classroom jottings
38. Little donkey
39. Identify
41. Part of RFD
43. Bridges or Brummel
44. Delay (2 wds.)
46. Daisy part
48. Water between the U.S. and Eur.
49. Princess Bea's father
51. Helped to commit a crime

53. Cheerleader's shout
55. Actress Campbell
56. Foggier
60. Fibbers
63. Angel's topper
64. Playground chute
66. Rummage __
68. Russia between 1917 and 1991 (abbr.)
69. Slightly warm
70. Where the princes schooled
71. "Love __ Bob"
72. Obstacle
73. Bastes

Down
1. Treasure hunter's need
2. Malaysia's continent
3. Thing
4. Sister of Moses
5. In __ flesh
6. Walk through water
7. Soccer stadium
8. Songwriter Neil
9. October's stone
10. Cats' prey
11. Beerlike brews
12. Primary color
14. Sandra Day __
20. Wide smile
22. Biting remark
24. Enjoy thoroughly (2 wds.)

26. Christmas gift-giver
27. Amtrak equipment
28. ___ to the teeth
30. Tiger baby
31. Unexpected pleasure
32. All steamed up
33. Had the ability to
36. Poet's "before"
37. The Devil
40. Belgium's cont.
42. Tagged
45. Perky
47. Tribe of Israel

50. Midsections
52. Harasses
54. Hayes or Hunt
56. Cattle feed
57. Ingrid, in "Casablanca"
58. Laundry verb
59. TV host Kelly
61. Appraise
62. ___ and steady
63. Island abode
65. Build a trench
67. Pulver's rank (abbr.)

CROSSWORD 26

Across

1. Actress Magnani
5. __ school
9. Hang loosely
12. Debatable
13. Correspondent Sawyer
14. Trumpeter Al
16. Guitar ridge
17. Gossiping busybody
18. Garfield's buddy
19. Slander
21. Produce, as wealth
23. Mauna __
24. Blow up
25. Biblical songs
28. Small river ducks
31. Brotherhood brother
32. Small, lacy mat
35. The Sphinx's home
37. Hideout
39. Nose, slangily
41. Great Lake
42. Building material
44. Fountain treats
46. Ky.'s neighbor
47. Singer Fisher
49. Pranks
51. Stinging comments
54. Religious sister
55. Buttonwood
58. Follows
62. Brown meat
63. Female opera stars
65. Engrossed
66. Starchy, edible root
67. Reviewer Roger
68. Pack cargo
69. Female fowl
70. Fender ding
71. Shipping weights

Down

1. Radio letters
2. "SNL" alum Dunn
3. Playwright Coward
4. Famed Hun
5. Slapstick missile
6. Stove
7. Go in
8. Goober
9. Deficit
10. Famous Verdi opera
11. Abrasive granules
13. Go-getters
15. Kickoff gadget
20. Love of King Midas
22. Fencing sword
25. Batter's place
26. Enjoyed the slopes
27. Moral offenses
29. Song line
30. Turns rapidly

31. Overhead railways
33. Brit's bathroom
34. "Star Wars" creature
36. Knight of "Caddyshack"
38. Snoopy's foe (2 wds.)
40. Brownest at the beach
43. Actor Neeson
45. Daze
48. Wore away gradually
50. Be emphatic about
52. Pay off
53. "The Magnificent __"
55. Former fast jet (abbr.)
56. Okey-doke
57. Be concerned
59. "Do __ others…"
60. Prince Harry's alma mater
61. Farm females
64. Picasso's field

CROSSWORD 27

Across

1. Large chunk
5. Play a part
8. Secluded valley
12. Actress Channing
14. __-a-brac
16. Singer Adams
17. Pedro's friend
18. Poetic "never"
19. "I've __ Around"
20. "Tell __ story" (2 wds.)
21. Distort from a true value
23. Planet after Saturn
25. __ group
26. Baked desserts
27. Ship's rear
29. Most optimistic
32. Square-dancing locales
33. Hanging piece
34. Struck
36. "__ Island with You" (2 wds.)
37. Stratum
38. Sporting cry
39. Banking machine (abbr.)
40. Ships' wheels
41. Run, as a color
42. Pacify
44. At __ for words (2 wds.)
45. Visitor to Siam
46. Finger noise
47. Loath
50. Pirate captain
51. New York time (abbr.)
54. Mr. Disney
55. Sounded the alarm
57. Bert's pal
59. Resembling
60. Svelte
61. Number of Disney's dwarfs
62. Yukon cab
63. Train depot (abbr.)
64. Bodybuilders' hangouts

Down

1. Con game
2. Limping
3. Pavarotti solo
4. Peat source
5. Daisy Mae's hubby
6. Workmen
7. Cravat
8. Degrade
9. Biblical locale
10. Stead
11. Camera glass
13. Forfeiters
15. Police car
22. Author Follett
24. Actor Wallace __
25. Teller's magician

partner
26. Scrutinizes
27. "__ Lucia"
28. Travel on foot
29. Nursery __
30. Loafers, e.g.
31. Wearies
32. Python's kin
33. Nacho chip dip
35. Nickname for
    Theodore
37. Horseshoes shots
38. Total failure
40. Chicks' moms

41. Grass pieces
43. Separated
44. As well as
46. Frat letter
47. Leather punches
48. Colorado ski resort
49. Actress Sommer
50. Make mittens
51. Begrudge
52. Per __
53. Hamilton bills
56. Pacino et al.
58. Standard (abbr.)

CROSSWORD 28

Across
 1. Not us
 5. Caught in the __
 8. Arden et al.
12. Antique
14. Stray
16. Actor Neeson of "Schindler's List"
17. "When __ Eyes Are Smiling"
18. Fuel source
19. Light color
20. Goes to bed
22. Receive willingly
24. Removable top
25. Break the engagement
26. Menu heading
30. Grow faint
31. Nile snake
34. Actor Ken
35. Secret newlywed
37. __ Miguel
38. Salon service
40. "__ Believer" (2 wds.)
41. High poker pair
43. Finish
44. Renounce
47. Some necklines
48. Briny deep
49. Drizzle
50. Unwilling
52. "__ we forget"
53. Make do
54. Unravel a secret message
57. Merged
61. Retirement accounts (abbr.)
62. On-line person
64. Trickles
66. French miss (abbr.)
67. __ shirt
68. Virtuous
69. Snaky creatures
70. Tampa __
71. Large number

Down
 1. Cycle start
 2. Mister (Ger.)
 3. Writer Wiesel
 4. "Gorillas in the __"
 5. Semicircular
 6. Dove's sounds
 7. Dam-building org.
 8. Vote in
 9. Wickedness
10. Wyatt __
11. Particle of soot
13. Kid
15. Screenwriter May
21. "__ and shine!"
23. Store employee
25. Home of sumo
26. Afflictions
27. Certain dress style (hyph.)

28. Gray or Lavin
29. Reply (abbr.)
30. "Wonder __"
31. "Lou Grant" star
32. Persons of learning
33. Sheriff's men
36. Lawful
39. Made a boo-boo
42. "__ Got Sixpence"
45. Relax (2 wds.)
46. __-home pay
51. Snake's poison
52. Comes in last

53. Judy's brother on "The Jetsons"
54. Roosevelt coin
55. Mystery writer Gardner
56. Shout
57. Actor Lugosi
58. The voice of __
59. Pound or Stone
60. Actor Cain
63. Heaving cry
65. Sneaky

CROSSWORD 29

Across

1. VW horn sound
5. Mem. of Congress
8. Soccer game highlight
12. Thomas ___ Edison
13. Shade of purple
15. Strong cord
16. In ___ of (instead of)
17. Chain mail
18. Biblical priest
19. Croquet need
21. Smears
23. Guinness of films
25. Unaffiliated voter (abbr.)
26. ___ de Triomphe
29. Unruly youngster
31. Discontinued
36. Israel's Meir
38. Genesis sailor
40. Actress Theda
41. Busy as ___ (2 wds.)
42. Regretful
43. Dishonest one
44. Small bottle
45. "___ ye!"
46. Thick, as fog
47. Tempt
49. Navajo foe
51. Newsman Koppel
52. Scrap of food
54. Small songbird
56. Court meeting
60. Overacted
64. Ore vein
65. Hygienist's urging
67. Disneyland feature
68. Funny ___
69. Pets' pests
70. Streetcar
71. Bandleader Kenton
72. Speedy jet (abbr.)
73. Half (prefix)

Down

1. Aromatic oil
2. Director Kazan
3. Daredevil Knievel
4. TV chef Deen
5. McCartney's title
6. Shade providers
7. Model Campbell
8. Actor Kinnear
9. Seep
10. Showery mos.
11. Grassy area
13. By and by
14. Like raw carrots
20. Napoleon's place of exile
22. JFK's predecessor
24. Light boat
26. Century plant
27. Batman's helper

28. Golf shoe projection
30. Holy scroll
32. Skilled
33. Actress Susan __ James
34. Rub out
35. Was brave
37. Sandwich store
39. Straight as an __
42. Word on a tin badge
46. Per __ (by the day)
48. Comic Bill's nickname
50. Hot off the __
53. Turnpike fees
55. South's opposite
56. Ashes
57. Poet St. Vincent Millay
58. Witnessed
59. Negative votes
61. Firestone product
62. Dutch cheese
63. Actress Moore
64. Pounds (abbr.)
66. Perched

CROSSWORD 30

Across

1. Vipers
5. Laos's continent
9. Melville captain
13. Tedious person
14. Task
16. "__ Ha'i"
17. Teachers at the prom, e.g.
19. Single thing
20. A DiMaggio brother
21. Victory letters
22. Major network
24. Football action
25. Knack
28. FBI agents (hyph.)
30. __ measure
31. Circle part
33. Lunar bodies
34. Jumped aside suddenly
35. Story of a life, for short
36. Bossy's home
37. Play part
38. Dr. or lbs., e.g..
39. It can follow lemon or lime
40. Coop perch
41. Statement of belief
42. Washington VIP (abbr.)
43. Loafing
44. Pan covers
45. Thingamabob
47. Installs carpeting
49. Vitality
50. Strong attachment
51. Old card game
54. "West Side Sotry" actress, with 29 Down
57. Miami stadium (2 wds.)
60. Diver's practice spot
61. Jury group
62. C.S.A.'s Robert __ (2 wds.)
63. Fall flowers
64. "__ goes nothing!"
65. Lauria and Quayle

Down

1. Start of a tot's song
2. District in London
3. London buggy
4. Between Aug. and Oct.
5. Farm measures
6. Sandals
7. Charged atoms
8. "How __ you?"
9. Treat badly
10. Leia's "Star Wars" hero
11. Boxer Muhammad
12. Nipped
15. Runaway
18. Cowgirl Dale
23. Ran, as colors
24. Quaker William

25. Sully
26. Nailed a crook
27. Sioux and Choctaw
28. Spurred
29. See 54 Across
30. Things at hand
32. Telephone __
33. Advanced degs.
34. Berate
37. Fizzy beverage (2 wds.)
38. Onassis and others
40. Go piggyback
41. "Bonnie and __"

46. Precious gems
47. Recluse
48. Corner formation
50. Ruin
51. "Damn Yankees" temptress
52. TV lawyer Marshall
53. Spanish "rahs"
54. Tachometer letters
55. Debt letters
56. News legend Brokaw
58. Rooter's cry
59. Sleeper's spot

CROSSWORD 31

Across
1. ___ kid (egghead)
5. Sachet scent
10. "X-Files" org.
13. Intl. pact
14. A miss is as good as ___ (2 wds.)
15. Swamp plant
16. Raised horses
17. "The First Noel," e.g.
18. James ___ Carter
19. Respect
21. Internet service (abbr.)
22. Creative
23. Melodies
25. Refrigerator contents
27. Fasten for a second time
30. Viscous mud
33. "Caught you!"
34. "Tell Mama" singer James
35. Handled
37. Singer Coolidge
39. German steel city
42. Used crayons
43. Prepared to propose
45. Tightly stretched
47. Heredity initials
48. ___ rings

50. District in Queens
52. "As Time ___ By"
54. Hence
55. Chili ingredient
58. "Quiet!"
60. Medicinal element
64. Fr. miss
65. Bother
67. Christmas
68. Feral
69. Language of Caesar
70. And others (2 wds.)
71. Utter
72. Upright
73. Talks nonsense

Down
1. Sheryl Swoopes's league (abbr.)
2. Like a diamond
3. Article
4. Belt of the heavens
5. Tear
6. "___ Man" (2 wds.)
7. Former coin of Italy
8. Unfriendly
9. Stringed instruments
10. Be apprehensive
11. Ernie's roommate
12. In a lazy manner
15. Got prepared
20. Anger
24. Speedy jets (abbr.)
26. "___ Yeller"
27. Savanna animal, for

short

28. Devoured

29. Spaghetti, e.g.

31. __ Gras (New Orleans event)

32. Actress Verdugo

33. Noah's craft

36. Former airline

38. Trued up

40. Alleviate

41. It enriches the body

44. "Never __ Late"

46. Take-out phrase (2

wds.)

49. Quik company

51. Comic Dangerfield

53. Cut, as wool

55. Yuppie cars

56. Director Kazan

57. Pact partner

59. Loathe

61. Small amount

62. Tide type

63. Building additions

66. "Get 'em, Rover!"

CROSSWORD 32

Across

1. Emulate a nomad
5. Letters on some tow trucks
8. Preowned
12. Margins
14. West Point (abbr.)
16. Slangy refusal
17. Kentucky frontiersman
18. "Shrek" star Cameron
19. Manitoba Indian
20. Buenos Aires's country (abbr.)
21. Perlman of "Cheers"
23. Like one taking forty winks
25. Tennis's Lendl
26. Choir voice
27. Sailed
30. Clydesdale's cries
33. Was ill
34. Trademark of George Burns
36. Summer, in Paris
38. __ dunk
39. Irritates
40. Wharf
41. Shorten pants
42. Ustinov or Sellers
43. Command
44. Medicine amount
46. Shuns
47. Sing high praises
48. Chomp
49. Make new ringlets
52. Pinocchio, for one
53. CIA's predecessor
56. Dutch cheese town
57. In need of irrigation
59. "Same here!"
61. Speak imperfectly
62. Marriage, e.g.
63. Garlic's relative
64. Pro votes
65. Berlin's land (abbr.)
66. Egyptian vipers

Down

1. C&W singer McEntire
2. Perfume
3. In eager desire
4. Fathers and uncles
5. Poet W.H.
6. The Far East
7. Doctors' gp.
8. Clear a drain blockage
9. Very achy
10. Duel tool
11. Far down
13. Did a waiter's job
15. Spring-flowering shrubs
22. Owned
24. __-fry
25. Filler
26. __ management
27. Wild party

28. Greased
29. Texas shrine
31. Shirley Temple film
32. Horse
34. Quoted
35. __ de France
37. Goes astray
39. Customary customer
40. Ship's bow
42. Steve Allen successor
43. Cook too long
45. Sudden declines
46. "Now I get it!"
48. Hayride beverage
49. Depend
50. Entertainer Adams
51. Pedro's house
52. Word on a lo-cal label
53. Singer Redding
54. "Whoa!"
55. Daughters' counterparts
58. Trucker's semi
60. "Back __ minute!" (2 wds.)

CROSSWORD 33

Across

1. Lunchtime favorites
5. Story about Zeus
9. Lifesaving skill (abbr.)
12. Cheer
13. Carved gem
14. Footgear
15. Water, in Madrid
16. Remove a lid
17. Potter's need
18. Polaris (2 wds.)
20. Penalized monetarily
21. "Do __ say…" (2 wds.)
22. Band instrument
24. Grime
27. Underscores
31. Evaded
33. "Bonanza" son
34. Cut the lawn
36. Greek letter
37. Land of pyramids
39. Scary Lugosi
40. Busy buzzer
41. Close forcibly
42. Gems
44. Made ready
47. Purposes
48. William __ ("Hopalong")
49. Mamie's hubby
51. Fall pumpkin coverer
54. Complete costumes
60. Wash
61. Foe
62. Waikiki picnic
63. "The doctor __" (2 wds.)
64. Hayworth and Moreno
65. Monster
66. Advanced degree (abbr.)
67. A cinch
68. Sobbed

Down

1. Grain coating
2. Identifying symbol
3. Guided trip
4. RBI, e.g.
5. Praying __ (insect)
6. Local community center (abbr.)
7. Earring shape
8. Bunny movement
9. Place for a goatee
10. North or South __
11. Tear asunder
13. Swear
14. Cleans the pool
19. Hardy
20. To-do
23. Relaxes

24. Snooze
25. __ space
26. Actress Lupino
28. Cooking herb
29. Correct copy
30. Sandal parts
31. Recede
32. Put off
35. Had been
38. Corsage flower
39. Singer __ Jovi
41. Notice
43. Abound

45. Entertainer Buddy
46. Alarm
50. Small islands
51. Gymnast's trick
52. Poison ivy reaction
53. Latin poet
55. Earns after taxes
56. Boxer's punch
57. European sled
58. Old West lawman
59. Beef fat
61. Before, poetically

CROSSWORD 34

Across

1. Young whale
5. WWII org.
8. In-box item
12. Diva's solo
13. Signed
15. "Beauty __ the eye…" (2 wds.)
16. True
17. "Plaza __"
18. Pathway
19. Sitting rooms
21. Disconnects a light
23. Geologic age
24. Steeple top
25. Cattle feeding troughs
28. Entertainer Ethel
32. Bull's mate
33. Type of dress (hyph.)
35. Indefinite amount
36. '30s relief agency (abbr.)
37. Quill tip
38. Sitcom interrupters
41. Jazzman Montgomery
42. Biting remark
44. Harpy
46. O'Toole's rank (abbr.)
47. Minister
50. Marzipan ingredients
52. Muslim religion
54. "Are you a man __ mouse?" (2 wds.)
55. Shorten
58. Breastbone
62. Unwrap
63. Musketeer's hat feature
65. Gossip purveyor Barrett
66. Was carried
67. Begat
68. Exclude
69. Singer Williams
70. SSW's opp.
71. Moistens

Down

1. Criticize
2. Space
3. Fibber
4. "How have the mighty __"
5. Load
6. __ mask
7. Framed (2 wds.)
8. Flour grinders
9. Bible twin
10. Basketball center Yao
11. Singles
13. Tel Aviv native
14. Dungaree fabric
20. __ grinder
22. Prior to (prefix)
24. 9-digit item (abbr.)

25. Aesop's message
26. Informed
27. Barbecue order
29. Cut the lawn
30. Prayer closings
31. Gangbuster Eliot
32. Cable choice (abbr.)
34. Noble title
39. Put back a grade
40. Vowed
43. Tabloid regular Spears
45. __ and cheese
48. "The Lady __ Tramp" (2 wds.)
49. Fasteners
51. Not wide
53. "It's __ the Game" (2 wds.)
55. Mrs. Dithers
56. "__ my word!"
57. Comic Foxx
58. Captain Hook's pirate
59. Alaskan port
60. Single item
61. Small rugs
64. Vase

CROSSWORD 35

Across

1. Ewe's mate
4. Leading man, e.g.
9. "Green __ and Ham"
13. Fifi's friends
15. Culpability
16. Disney fish
17. Animal rights gp.
18. Underwear name
19. Fresh way to start
20. New Jersey city
22. __ Own (salad dressing)
24. Mournful song
26. Edison's inits.
27. "Duke of __"
29. Social Security no.
31. Overjoyed
34. Prisoner
36. "Hush!"
38. Flat-bottomed boat
40. R-V connection
41. Concorde's inits.
43. Journey segment
45. Furrowing tool
46. Netting
48. Oinking animal
50. Manufacturers
52. Not fake
54. Sunday seat
56. Bunk and twin
57. Trucker's semi
59. Primary
61. Maxim
65. Retires for the night (2 wds.)
69. Icicle place
70. Like a rainbow
72. Ticklish Muppet
73. Twilight times
74. Supermarket section
75. Forfeiture
76. Fasting season
77. Collar stiffeners
78. Misery

Down

1. Enthralled
2. The "A" in U.S.A. (abbr.)
3. Speck
4. Despise
5. Rings a trolley's bell
6. Make leather
7. Black cat, e.g.
8. Trip-meter button
9. Applies glossy paint
10. Rowlands of film
11. Feds (hyph.)
12. Piglets' mothers
14. Actress Dee
21. Inclines
23. Puppy's tail motion
25. 19th letter
27. Walk right in
28. Keep in stitches
30. Hockey org.

32. Pained
33. Rooms' entrances
34. Suffix for a doctrine
35. Psychic's letters
37. Dress edge
39. Director Craven
42. Advice
44. Zsa Zsa's last name
47. Autumn reaping
49. Precious stone
51. Bit of corn
53. Commit perjury
55. Needing thickener

58. Alumni, for short
60. Garland and Blume
61. Banana's skin
62. Favorable review
63. Kitchen hot spot
64. Annoying child
66. Gradual
67. "__ Lonesome I Could Cry" (2 wds.)
68. Cyrano's prominent feature
71. Top-secret U.S. org.

CROSSWORD 36

Across

1. Newsman Brinkley
6. College placement exams (abbr.)
10. Basketball hoop edge
13. Mirror reflection
14. Gps. that organize book sales and bake sales
15. British farewell (2 wds.)
16. Sun shield
17. "Oh, sure!" (2 wds.)
18. That being the case (2 wds.)
19. Summer cooler
20. Vamp Theda
22. Hoagie
24. Cockpit occupants
26. Take a breather
29. Slumbering
32. Camper's stake (2 wds.)
35. Single items
36. "Heads or __?"
38. Actor Linden
39. Not any
40. Motor coaches
41. "__ Le Moko"
42. __ the line
43. Performs a dairy farm chore
44. Composer Copland
45. Dessert at an Italian eatery

47. Graphics within pictures
48. Sail support
49. Tibetan animals
52. Go downhill
54. Camping equipment
55. Chicago player
58. Champagne color
61. 2002, to Brutus
63. Pursue
65. Top aviators
66. Survey
67. Derby entrant
68. Bread type
69. Envisions
70. Feel longing

Down

1. Aria singer
2. Between
3. Posy holder
4. "Here __ again!" (2 wds.)
5. Some races
6. Ex-veep Agnew
7. Ready to bunt (2 wds.)
8. Light bulb inventor's monogram
9. Fast jets (abbr.)
10. English fliers (abbr.)
11. "__ a miracle!"
12. __ Tse-tung
15. Lhasa's country
21. High mountain
23. Coffee vessels
24. Tennis legend Sampras
25. Pens

27. Globe
28. "I'm a little __…"
29. Mom's sisters
30. Busybodies
31. Form a queue (2 wds.)
33. City rails
34. Valleys
36. Dutch bloom
37. Pose a question
40. Storage container
41. Say "no thanks"
43. "__ & Mindy"
44. Political disorder

46. Facial disguises
47. Boise's state (abbr.)
50. Dexterous
51. Diamond and Simon
53. Little devils
55. Actress Irene
56. "Back in the __" (Beatles)
57. Existed
58. Golf goal
59. Cold and unfriendly
60. Born
62. Curly's cohort
64. Remove weeds

CROSSWORD 37

Across

1. Hair detangler
5. Every
9. Housemaid's __
13. U.S. citizen (abbr.)
14. Logging result
16. Particle
17. "Tomb Raider" heroine
18. Prohibition
19. Comedian Sahl
20. Distributes the cards again
22. Rings up
24. NFL's Rozelle
25. Lohan's "__ Girls"
26. For a short period
29. Bale storage area
32. Dinghies
33. Richard Burton's homeland
34. Bandleader Brown
36. Londoner, for short
37. Supper morsel
38. Fido's treat
39. Height (abbr.)
40. Mighty particles
42. Untethered
43. Leaves behind, slangily
45. Huge mobs
46. Surrounded by
47. Allow usage
48. Tin alloy
51. Weirdest
54. Descended
55. __ and Gomorrah
57. Betsy or Diana
59. "The Sun __ Rises"
60. Singer Lopez
61. Isaac's son
62. "__ Man" (1984 film)
63. Take time out
64. Take a risk

Down

1. Pres. Coolidge
2. Sharif or Bradley
3. A __ trifle
4. Shiloh's daddy (2 wds.)
5. Squire's property
6. "__ of Two Cities" (2 wds.)
7. Young lions
8. Insurance plan option (abbr.)
9. Japanese robe
10. One 12 o'clock
11. To be (Fr.)
12. Diner sign
15. Bluto's rival
21. Slippery creatures
23. Holbrook and others
25. Fountain drinks
26. Swedish rock group
27. Earth

28. Port-au-Prince's location
29. Injures
30. Huge overflow
31. Edgy
33. Courted
35. Espies
38. Edged
40. Top
41. Need for water
42. Anderson of "Nurses"
44. Skin picture

45. __ crab
47. Jaworski and Trotsky
48. Carson's predecessor
49. Noted fashion magazine
50. Hair strand
51. Falco or Adams
52. Baseballer Sammy
53. Romanov ruler
56. Bobby of the Bruins
58. "A Boy Named __"

CROSSWORD 38

Across

1. Slightly open
5. Conceit
10. Address book abbr.
13. Golfer's shout
14. Flaxen material
15. Flower holder
16. Like (2 wds.)
17. Aunt's hubby
18. Naughty children
19. Feel indignant
21. Deli meat
22. Small hollow
23. Shingle site
25. Where shares are traded (abbr.)
27. Dessert selections
29. Military mail abbr.
31. Acts as emcee
35. Mentally healthy
36. AFL's partner
37. Capital of Russia
38. Birthday number
39. Soup stock vegetable
41. Greek letter
42. Trial balloon
44. Made a lap
45. Obstacle
46. Comedian Murphy
47. Panhandle
48. Singer Billy
49. Inits. for Lopez
51. Appear
53. Actress Theda
56. Baseball Giant Mel
58. Simmered
62. Company head (abbr.)
63. Things
65. Own
66. Pub orders
67. Pluck
68. Keats poems
69. Uncle or cousin (abbr.)
70. Grasps
71. Bandleader Lawrence

Down

1. Distant
2. Baseball's Canseco
3. Onassis and namesakes
4. Football figure
5. Disney dog
6. __ Tin Tin
7. Narrow margin
8. The "D" in FDR
9. Yank, to a Reb
10. Tone down
11. Sports lover's cable choice
12. In case
15. Movies on tape
20. Numerals (abbr.)
24. State festival
26. Go marketing

27. Summoned
28. "__ You" (Beatle song, 2 wds.)
30. Deputized band
32. Drama unit
33. Full amount
34. Burglar's haul
35. Secure
36. Subaru or Toyota
37. Major engineering school (abbr.)
39. Bird sound
40. Scolds
43. Spring flowers

45. One way or another
47. Cake mixture
48. NY footballer
50. Auctioneer's word
52. Hairpin curves
53. Yogi __
54. Wheel spindle
55. Whirl
57. Garr or Hatcher
59. Slugger Boggs
60. Motorcyclist Knievel
61. School table
64. Best on a team (abbr.)

CROSSWORD 39

Across

1. Lifesaving skill (abbr.)
4. Attention-getting sound
8. Jimmy Carter's alma mater (abbr.)
12. Basketball need
14. Scarlett's surname
16. Low tide
17. Moffo of the Met
18. Tightened a corset
19. Wide reaching
20. Actress Cannon
21. Aggravate
22. "Laughing" beasts
24. "Moby-__"
26. Son of Jacob and Leah
27. In music, from do to do
30. Neglectful
34. At hand
35. Olympic events
36. Actor Morrow
37. Tuna holder
38. Leaks
39. Dental gp.
40. Psychic Geller
41. Small birds
42. Poet W.H. __
44. Make a replica
46. "Gunsmoke" star
47. Role in "Casablanca"
48. Outing
49. Rebel
52. __-de-sac
53. Actress Dalton
57. Newspaper item, for short
58. Foolish
60. Pepsi flavor
61. Ashen
62. Group of witches
63. Model Heidi
64. Gazed upon
65. Actor Richard __
66. Hosp. employees

Down

1. Piece of a Florida ballot
2. Stable resident
3. Gossip columnist Barrett
4. Keep order
5. "Jaws" villain
6. Bag
7. Three (Ital.)
8. Disclose
9. Penn or Astin
10. Apollo agcy.
11. Rental abodes (abbr.)
13. Tibetan creatures
15. Clings (to)
23. __ Saint Laurent
25. Possessive

contraction
26. Lighting fixtures
27. Come to pass
28. ___ Boothe Luce
29. Pick-me-up
30. Actor Michael
31. Elude
32. Agrees (with)
33. Peruses quickly
35. Garbo of films
38. Severe
41. Healthy
42. Onassis, for short
43. Empty luggage

45. Rampaged
46. Dahl or Francis
48. Part of a stereo set
49. 1948 Hitchcock thriller
50. On-line auction house
51. Loathsome
52. Underground chamber
54. Intrepid
55. Smear
56. Orange tubers
59. Holiday party drink

CROSSWORD 40

Across

1. Scientists' rms.
5. Gust of wind
9. Fundamentals
13. Evils
14. Rewrite
15. Tater state
16. Debatable
17. Eye protector
18. Prize for Al Gore
19. Prim one's coiffure
20. Meddles (with)
22. Stun
23. Weirdest
25. Utter defeat
27. Vocalist Frankie
30. Disapproving sounds
34. Butter-makers, at times
37. Girl Scout's group
38. Denials
39. Hold session
40. Garcia of "Project Runway"
41. Intertwined fabric
43. Sneering
46. Designer Klein
48. Pounce (down on)
49. Be worthy of
51. Prayer beads
55. "__ Only Love"
58. Giggled
61. Poor grade
62. Pageant category
64. Pairs
65. "...__ good night" (2 wds.)
66. Eyed flirtatiously
67. Watson of "Harry Potter"
68. So-so
69. Sweet palm fruit
70. Exude
71. Drill attachments

Down

1. "How-low-can-you-go" dance
2. Orally
3. Like many Swedes
4. Concorde's initials
5. Aspic ingredient
6. Abel's father
7. "Thpeak like thith"
8. Old-fashioned anesthetic
9. Confusion
10. Ali __
11. Gnaw
12. Shoe part
15. Slur
20. Russian dictator
21. Eden __
24. Slippery
26. Root vegetables
28. Capone's enemy
29. Sevareid and Clapton

31. Invent a word
32. Hong __
33. Mineral spring
34. Mrs. Dithers of "Blondie"
35. Become well
36. Store
38. "The More You Know" network
42. Started a phone call, once
44. Predicted
45. Five basic __ groups
47. Gun lobby (abbr.)
50. Art class models
52. Candidate Stevenson
53. Ignited anew
54. Anniversary count
55. Music lover's gadget
56. Roman garb
57. Loose sediment
59. Oscar-winning role for Hanks
60. Baseball plate
63. Witness
65. Andrews, for one (abbr.)

CROSSWORD 41

Across

1. Cherrystone, e.g.
5. Isn't, incorrectly
9. Johann Sebastian ___
13. Hawkeye State
14. Short
16. Painful
17. Roger Rabbit, e.g.
18. Serious
19. Hit first feetfirst
20. Animate
22. Roman sea god
24. Fish flippers
25. Shoe width
26. Appearance
29. Medium, e.g.
31. Pleasingly plump
34. Decided between things
35. Mailman, at times
36. Batter's stat
37. Slant
38. Extreme anger
39. Sir's female counterpart
40. Conger
41. Ferber et al.
43. Retinue
44. Hosp. figures
45. Rivals
46. Bank worker
47. Mature pullet
48. Brewing ingredient
49. Toppers for Dick Tracy
53. Initially (2 wds.)
57. Smile
58. Valentine symbol
60. Pinnacle
61. Lease
62. Mink's relative
63. Comic Jay
64. Printing fluids
65. Guide
66. Antlered animals

Down

1. Reference
2. "Crazy" bird
3. On the lam, military style
4. Obvious
5. Not in attendance
6. Wrinkle chasers
7. Penpoint
8. New driver, usually
9. Tend to a roast
10. Controversial rights gp.
11. Goatee's spot
12. Jekyll's alter ego
15. Deep ___
21. Bad habit
23. British noble

26. Took steps
27. Not as outgoing
28. Balloting places
29. Actress Gilbert et al.
30. Treats a sprain
31. Delicate
32. Taper off
33. Kitchen device
35. Coal source
39. __-choice test
41. Continually
42. Shore and
    Washington

43. Ego
46. Created lace
47. Whets
48. One Mrs. Trump
49. Alphabetic quartet
50. Actress Moran
51. Long dagger
52. Aquatic mammal
54. Filmstrip unit
55. Descended slowly
56. Boxing outcomes
    (abbr.)
59. Actor Vigoda

CROSSWORD 42

Across

1. __ radio (hyph.)
5. Nerds' kin
10. Go a-courting
13. Singer Falana
14. Of legal age
15. "__ Zapata!"
16. Move quickly
17. Mrs. Tom Cruise
18. Actor Estrada
19. Fume
21. Summer hue
22. Beatty and others
23. Leftovers dish
25. __ too pleased
27. Ran
29. Tenth mo.
31. Discontinue
35. Barrymore of "Fever Pitch"
36. Modern diagnostic test (abbr.)
37. Control
38. Intention
39. Has tremors from excitement
41. Used a stool
42. Designer Ralph
44. IM provider
45. Strop
46. Baseball mistake
47. Heston's gp.
48. Insurance agents (abbr.)
49. Quick snack
51. Letters on a rocket
53. Star followers
56. Clergy member (abbr.)
58. Sharpens a razor
62. Economist Greenspan
63. Mrs. Archie Bunker
65. Pig's dinner
66. Baby foxes
67. Borden animal
68. Drink for Juan
69. Paris summer
70. Stitches
71. Knitting necessity

Down

1. Elevations (abbr.)
2. Larger amount
3. Floating ice mass
4. New Testament book
5. Arouses
6. Director Lupino
7. "__ and Jeff"
8. Flexible
9. Office worker, for short
10. Metal string
11. Roman poet
12. Former acorns
15. Gloss
20. "I've __ enough!"
24. Rhino's feature

26. Mark Harmon series
27. Monastery brother
28. Monkey's cousin
30. White Owl product
32. Fable collector
33. Reads quickly
34. Diminutive suffix
35. Chip's chipmunk pal
36. 1/60 of an hr.
37. Singer Shannon
39. Garr of "Tootsie"
40. Bank transaction
43. Spring birds
45. Rumor

47. Sewing item
48. Q followers
50. Squirrels' homes
52. Campfire leftovers
53. Construct
54. Disembarked
55. Stadium entrance
57. Passport endorsement
59. Gymnast Korbut
60. Precipitate heavily
61. Bridge part
64. Actor Robbins

CROSSWORD 43

Across

1. Sounds of disgust
5. Messy places
10. Upsets
14. TV actor Hayes
15. Basketball's Shaq
16. Genesis sailor
17. One against
18. Like a fish
19. Cooked enough
20. Nolan Ryan pitch
22. Small flutes
23. Era
24. Nation's banner
26. Wobble
30. Downsizer's actions
34. Circumvent
35. Pays attention to
37. Seamstress's target
38. Folding beds
39. Nautical "yes"
40. Mongolian desert
41. Supper scrap
42. Anxieties
44. "Cheaper by the __"
45. Just barely (3 wds.)
47. Recording studio controls
48. Singer Arnold
49. Sotheby's offer
50. Hoaxes
53. Fell back to a former worse state
58. Early bird's prize
59. Purple __
61. Parisian pronoun
62. Have __ in one's bonnet (2 wds.)
63. Eden fruit
64. Drought's lack
65. Garden amphibian
66. Sci-fi weapon
67. Wharton grads

Down

1. Milit. branch
2. Actress Rowlands
3. Berets and bonnets
4. Peevish mood
5. Medicinal measure
6. Wiggily or Sam
7. Dinner, e.g.
8. Comrade
9. Foxlike
10. "Mood __" (Duke Ellington tune)
11. Santa's landing spot
12. "Citizen __"
13. Women
21. Like some eagles
22. Bainter and Wray
24. Runs away
25. Young Highlander
26. Father of Joseph
27. Africa's __ Coast
28. Must, slangily
29. Enlisted men, for

short

31. Turned to ice
32. Filament
33. Whirls
35. Newsman Reasoner
36. "Peeper"
40. Jupiter, e.g.
42. Low fellows
43. Assist
44. Baby word
46. __ and hawed
47. Water purifier
49. Comic Milton

50. Kill flies
51. Boxcar rider
52. Telephone __ code
53. Taps lightly
54. Curl maker, for short
55. Piece of concrete
56. Director Kazan
57. Hideaways
59. Linden of "Barney Miller"
60. Smog-watching agcy.

CROSSWORD 44

Across

1. Burnt residue
4. Societal newcomers
8. Lama's country
13. Wild hog
15. Fashion model Macpherson
16. Stevenson of Illinois
17. Hay unit
18. Sir's counterpart
19. Slips over without emphasis
20. Its flight was commanded by James Lovell (2 wds.)
23. Actress Skye
24. "__ a Rebel"
25. Morley of "60 Minutes"
28. Obligation
31. Cleopatra's snake
34. Desire
35. __-dropper
37. Milk amount (abbr.)
38. Barbara Eden TV show (4 wds.)
42. Competitor
43. "WKRP" alum Anderson
44. Davis of "Stuart Little"
45. Tax inits.
46. Makes lace
48. Indexes
49. Kit __ Club ("Cabaret")
51. Fashion designer Cassini
53. WWII miniseries (3 wds.)
60. Tragic teen lover
61. __-tat-tat (hyph.)
62. Like a villain
63. More aloof
64. Not up
65. Surrealism's Salvador
66. Outdated
67. Koppel and Turner
68. Actor Beatty

Down

1. Israel's Eban
2. Laundry detergent
3. Angelic accessory
4. Little devil
5. On cloud nine
6. Uninteresting
7. Teamster's truck
8. Sip
9. Goofs off
10. "My __ Heaven"
11. Sweat for
12. It is, poetically
14. Release from duty
21. Mascara brand
22. Compose verse
25. Genre for "Star

Trek" (hyph.)

26. Fervor
27. Bus drivers' collections
29. Not suited
30. ___ Mahal
31. De Mille of dance
32. Peter or Paul, e.g.
33. Appeals
36. Young bird of prey
39. Slogan
40. ___ wing and a prayer (2 wds.)
41. Spoke like steeds

47. Arranged
49. Knobby joints
50. Cherish
52. Burdens
53. ___ Raton, Florida
54. French friends
55. Campus gp.
56. Talking movie piglet
57. Writer Hunter
58. Agitate
59. Reached base feetfirst
60. Sleepy Van Winkle

CROSSWORD 45

Across

1. Garden plots
5. Famous __ words
9. Manicurist's tool
13. Door out
14. Undo sneakers
16. Federal agent (hyph.)
17. Rigging support
18. Growl
19. Hover
20. Ohio port of entry
22. Swarming
24. Leaning Tower locale
26. Movie-at-home format (abbr.)
27. Tabby, e.g.
30. Tremor, slangily
32. Mountaineer's climb
37. Tolerate
39. Ink spot
41. Acknowledge
42. Mention
43. Yard divider
44. Nip
45. "Clueless" catch phrase (2 wds.)
46. Ogled
47. Cosmetician Lauder
48. Account book
50. Funnyman Foxx
52. Do sums
53. Gambler's marker
55. Hounds
57. Calling up
61. Stockings
65. Air __
66. Chastise
68. Skater's jump
69. Cardinal, e.g.
70. Singer Osmond
71. Note
72. Mid-month day
73. Squint
74. Stuck-up one

Down

1. Number one
2. Pre-2005 Montreal athlete
3. Watch face
4. Throat infection
5. "Dracula" star
6. Columnist Landers
7. Doctor's "right away!"
8. All in
9. Alphabetic quartet
10. "__ Old Cowhand" (2 wds.)
11. Director Fritz
12. Manchester's locale (abbr.)
15. Exalt
21. Dingy bar
23. Physicians (abbr.)
25. Westminster __
27. Panama, for one

28. Put down
29. Meek
31. Older
33. Hansoms
34. A Peron
35. Famed
36. Wool weave
38. C followers
40. David __ Stiers
43. Bravery
47. Fretful
49. One, in Berlin
51. Anger
54. Open a bottle
56. Closes violently
57. __ in full
58. Employ
59. Probability relative
60. 2000 Presidential candidate
62. Draft animals
63. Pixar clown fish
64. Untidy person
65. Slugger's goal (abbr.)
67. Tell untruths

CROSSWORD 46

Across
1. New Year's song beginning
5. British fliers' gp.
8. Dwelling
12. Sweeper's tool
14. Glazier's material
15. Claim
16. Numbers game
17. Diamond hit (2 wds.)
19. "Take Me __ Am" (2 wds.)
20. Lend
22. More unusual
23. Tyne of "Cagney & Lacey"
24. __ extinguisher
26. Baseball figure
29. Lassie and Toto, e.g.
32. Weeper's output
33. Small combos
34. Cariou or Deighton
36. Circle segments
37. __ terrier
38. Cooing bird
39. Hurry
40. Creates
41. First-rate
42. Mounted policeman
44. Heed
45. Great benefit
46. Kill
47. Off
50. Window part
51. Ace
54. Lurching
57. Actor Robert
59. Selves
60. Lena of "Alias"
61. "__ I Don't Have You"
62. Loud noises
63. Was introduced to
64. Fr. holy women

Down
1. Swedish pop group
2. Author Leon __
3. Actress Anderson
4. Puppy
5. Precipitate
6. Actress Sothern
7. Attorney's retainer
8. Set
9. Ancient Roman poet
10. Relocate
11. Water pitcher
13. Teeth for grinding
14. DVD button
18. Singer Day
21. Madrid cheer
23. SSW and ENE, e.g.
24. Country exhibitions
25. Hip to (2 wds.)
26. Mormon state
27. Earn
28. Trotter
29. Colonial news

bringer
30. Secretly wed
31. Lucky number
33. Accepted
35. Misfit
37. Guitar neck
attachment
38. Assignment
40. Antlered animal
41. Tracks game
43. Preoccupy intensely
44. Entire amount
46. Posted direction

47. Scored 100%
48. "The Gift of the __"
49. Strong metal
50. Agitated mood
51. Shut in
52. Chinese restaurant
staple
53. Single units
55. Name (Fr.)
56. __ du Diable (Devil's
Island)
58. Fleur-de-__

CROSSWORD 47

Across

1. Broadsides
5. Hebrew judge
8. End-of-week initials
12. On the Baltic
13. Football hero Rockne
15. Chinese staple
16. "__ keep" (procrastinator's motto)
17. Sharpened
18. Had a birthday
19. Contradict
21. Letterman and Copperfield
23. Darn socks
24. Innings count, usually
25. Regard highly
28. Ladybugs, e.g.
31. Jackie O's second husband
32. __ macaroni
34. Genders
36. Finger ornament
38. Kinds
40. Actor Auberjonois
41. Cloth fold
43. Birds' homes
45. Trio after Q
46. Miracle place in France

48. Flat dishes
50. __-do-well
51. Take the yacht
52. Witch tricker of a tale
55. Window covers
59. Brunch or lunch
60. Complete amount
62. Hymn end
63. Different
64. John Quincy __
65. Philbin's co-host
66. No, to Yuri
67. Coloring substance
68. Traffic sign

Down

1. Incursion
2. Italian sparkling wine
3. Blanc and Brooks
4. Genoa sausage
5. Finalized
6. European sled
7. Ending for suburban or meteor
8. Wayfarer
9. Leslie Caron film
10. Covered a cake
11. Govt. agents
13. Edible nut parts
14. "Frasier" pooch
20. Actor Richard of "Sommersby"
22. Insect pests
24. Salamanders

25. Senior citizens' org.
26. Power tool
27. Sal of "Rebel Without a Cause"
28. Uninteresting people
29. Put forth effort
30. Understanding
33. Blunder
35. Collections
37. Protective glove
39. London cathedral (2 wds.)
42. Timber source

44. Gash
47. Actress Burke
49. Church tables
51. "___ on you!"
52. FBI agents (hyph.)
53. Trust
54. Lighten
55. Halt
56. Pour forth
57. "___ Man" (1984 film)
58. Clothes fastener
61. Weird

CROSSWORD 48

Across

1. Abby, to Ann
5. Bit of bread crust
10. __ and coo
14. MasterCard rival
15. __ beam
16. Sheriff Taylor's boy
17. Know-it-__
18. Last Greek letter
19. 1916 Lopez hit
20. Drinking vessels
22. TV's "__ Camera"
24. Newspaper inserts
25. Simple
26. Speaks like a Southern belle
30. More refined
33. Painter's prop
34. Kathy of "Misery"
35. Josh
37. Fine spray
38. Figure __
39. Lilt
40. Lennon's widow Yoko
41. Muffles
42. Slip backward
43. Winter driver's need
45. Hub
46. Expressions of disgust
47. 10/31 shout
48. Artist's workshop
51. Discontinuing
55. Shredded
56. Slacken
58. Sandwich shop
60. Scrambled items
61. Actress Cara
62. __-steven
63. Versifier
64. Traverse
65. Grain

Down

1. Federal power inits.
2. Cager Chamberlain
3. Rhodes, e.g.
4. Space explorers (abbr.)
5. Cumulus, cirrus, etc.
6. Inclined ways
7. Capitalizes on
8. Actress Tilly
9. Jewelry box item
10. Headpiece
11. MP3 player from Apple
12. "Darling __"
13. Sleuth's clue
21. Visit
23. Onassis and Meyers
25. Wool eaters
26. Auto dealer's model
27. "Casablanca" star Claude
28. Organization (abbr.)
29. Drenched
30. Professional's

beeper
31. Break forth
32. Dentist's direction
34. Nips
36. Root __
38. Exhilirated
39. Sunbather's goal
41. Wise men
42. Durocher and Carroll
44. Least mannerly
45. Cajoles
47. Legumes

48. Dancer's move
49. Fast food request (2 wds.)
50. Insist upon
51. Egyptian queen, informally
52. The __ of March
53. "Party of Five" actress Campbell
54. Great joy
57. Go wrong
59. Not Rep. or Dem.

CROSSWORD 49

Across

1. Strikebreaker
5. Make corrections
10. __ le Pew
14. O'Hara plantation
15. __ plexus
16. Declare
17. Emanate
18. Stable youngsters
19. Ascend
20. Vicki Lewis and Kathy Griffin, e.g.
22. Seasons food
23. Raps gently
24. __ drum
26. Flawed
29. One to a __
33. European car
34. Plant stem
36. "Ooh-__" (hyph.)
37. Music or painting
38. Bolivia's neighbor (abbr.)
39. Truck-maker's inits.
40. Nick and Nora's pooch
42. Concluded
44. Hook's right hand
45. Santa's entryways
47. __ G. Robinson
49. Lugosi of films
50. Very top
51. Talk __ a minute (2 wds.)
54. Skyscraper necessity
58. Anderson of "WKRP"
59. Casaba, e.g.
61. Printing error, informally
62. Unknown author (abbr.)
63. The "A" in NBA (abbr.)
64. Stretches out
65. Chanted
66. Like spinach
67. Declare untrue

Down

1. Sterling (abbr.)
2. Attended
3. Extremely dry
4. Soaking spot
5. Eludes captors
6. States of mind
7. Building wings
8. Natalie Cole's dad
9. "ER" characters
10. Sunshade
11. Corrupt
12. Fence support
13. Woolly mamas
21. Listening requirement
22. Fast jet (abbr.)
24. Protrude
25. Request

26. Soul singer Hayes
27. Swampy land
28. Singer LaBelle
29. Birthday greetings
30. Volcanic substance
31. Fudd of cartoons
32. Ran competitively
35. Country star Tucker
41. Walking casually
42. Snaky swimmer
43. Respectability
44. Perspired
46. Maiden name indicator

48. License-testing place (abbr.)
50. Emotionally distant
51. Poetic lament
52. Lisa of the Louvre
53. Party to (2 wds.)
54. Actress Lanchester
55. Little kid
56. "__ sesame!"
57. Blushing
59. Bad (prefix)
60. Wind direction (abbr.)

CROSSWORD 50

Across

1. Between
5. Questions
9. Strip of contention
13. Tortilla sandwich
14. Use a rotisserie
16. Teheran's country
17. Clip neatly
18. Biblical food
19. Tangerine skin
20. Island (Fr.)
21. Sports shoe name
22. Throb
24. Certain copies
26. Winner's place
27. Leos' mo.
28. Former capital of West Germany
29. Have title to
32. Oak tree starter
35. Ensigns
36. Neckwear piece
37. Minivans' kin
38. Fissures
39. "It was __ dream" (2 wds.)
40. Fury
41. Arkin and King
42. Nap
43. HST's preceder
44. Harmless prank
45. Advanced degree (abbr.)
46. Jogs along
48. Become sunny (2 wds.)
52. Singer Hill
53. Deceives
54. "Diamonds __ Forever"
55. Flat-bottomed boats
56. Juan Peron's wife
58. Omelet needs
59. Scallion's cousin
60. Movie parts
61. Monthly division
62. Corrals
63. Narrow's opposite
64. Pianist Duchin

Down

1. Garret
2. Actress Gibbs of "The Jeffersons"
3. More unfriendly
4. DeLuise or DiMaggio
5. Providing weapons
6. Drenches
7. Carol of "Scrooged"
8. ID digits
9. Maidens
10. Greek thinker
11. Writer Grey
12. Pairing word
15. Recording sessions
21. "Thing" word
23. Vases
25. Gin joints

26. Froths
28. Empty
30. ___ E. Coyote
31. Lowest tide
32. Like (2 wds.)
33. Part of Miss Muffet's meal
34. Surpassed
35. Is apprehensive
38. Spread on thickly
39. Hawkeye's portrayer
41. "Thanks ___!" (2 wds.)
42. Females

45. Say ___ and thank you
47. Chances
48. Mentioned
49. Acted violently
50. Pressed
51. Like a fly
52. Uncaged
53. Actress Taylor of "Mystic Pizza"
55. Swiss peak
57. Pledge
58. Flock female

CROSSWORD 51

Across
1. At a snail's __
5. Dirt
9. __-daisy
13. English nobleman
14. Use a swear word
15. __ bomb
16. Walked on
17. Ford lemon
18. Mimi and Nicole, to Tom Cruise
19. Comes into view
21. Author Stevenson's monogram
23. French island
24. Corset stiffener
25. Maps within maps
27. Habit
30. Certain exercise (hyph.)
32. Famed Giant Mel
33. Golden-touch king
35. Gets strikes or spares
39. Homeless child
41. Red carpet regular, for short
43. Pup's wagger
44. Indicate indifference
46. Saturate
48. Teachers' gp.
49. Eighteen-wheelers
51. Unavailable (2 wds.)
53. Photographic equipment
56. Dancer Verdon
57. Fruit drink
58. Batting sport's inits.
60. Rooftop sights
64. __ dry eye in the house (2 wds.)
66. Very angry
68. Expanded
69. The luck of the __
70. Presented with
71. Scanty skirt length
72. Cry out
73. Requirement
74. Eden outcast

Down
1. Animal rights gp.
2. Senior citizens' org.
3. Cut short
4. First-born child
5. Like a bubble bath
6. __ Fields cookies
7. Utilizer
8. __ like it is (2 wds.)
9. Colorado Indian
10. Elf's kin
11. Small food fish
12. Positive responses
14. Like tile
20. Particle
22. Ignore socially
26. Name for a Dalmatian
27. Intimidates

28. 2002 Olympics host
29. Ado
30. Seasons popcorn
31. "___ the light!" (2 wds.)
34. TV's Arnaz
36. Magician's prop
37. In ___ of (replacing)
38. Strike smartly
40. Combine together
42. Betwixt and ___
45. Origin
47. Bridge support
50. Slander

52. Mystery
53. Trick-or-treater's booty
54. Be nuts about
55. Iron or aluminum
56. Like certain communities
59. Soft French cheese
61. Extra dry
62. Singer Horne
63. Do the crawl
65. Carpenter's tool
67. Wide rdwy.

CROSSWORD 52

Across

1. In that event (2 wds.)
5. Sloping approaches
10. Ranch unit
14. Like a dishrag
15. Simpleton
16. "__ River"
17. Censor
18. Flat dish
19. Thin nail
20. Established
21. __ alai
22. Lazy folks
24. Carson's successor
26. Kopell of "The Love Boat"
29. Decent
31. Put lace around a border
35. Starts
38. Rudiments
40. Sailor's yes
41. Charity
42. Ishmael's mother
44. Coat-hanger material
45. Teacher's group (abbr.)
46. Now's partner
47. Famed rapper
49. Columbus's birthplace
51. Vinegar dispensers
53. Selected
55. At no time, poetically
58. Car racing org.
61. Elected ones
63. On the __ (fleeing)
65. First Amendment gp.
66. Wacky
69. Edison's middle name
70. Grandstand part
71. Hideous monsters
72. Legal claim on property
73. Ten to one, e.g.
74. Not those
75. Capri, e.g.

Down

1. Islands (Fr.)
2. Cuba's __ Castro
3. Strike, Biblically
4. Choose
5. Kelly of morning TV
6. Works without a script
7. Soccer player Hamm
8. Melting __
9. Ale holder
10. Sauntered
11. Pineapple center
12. Simba's sound
13. Means justifiers, sometimes
21. Part of JFK
23. Quits, as a battery
25. "JAG" spin-off
27. Cabinet with open shelves
28. Country singer McEntire
30. Tennis great Arthur

32. Profit
33. Brontë's "Jane ___"
34. Regard
35. Loud noise
36. C.S.A.'s Robert (2 wds.)
37. FBI agent (hyph.)
39. North American Indian
43. Circle portions
44. Sensible
46. Laugh sounds (2 wds.)
48. Peaks (abbr.)
50. Comes about

52. Joins forces
54. Whether ___ (2 wds.)
56. Designer Perry
57. Untwist
58. Treaty org.
59. Hydrochloric ___
60. Winter coaster
62. Wall Street market (abbr.)
64. Lion's headpiece
67. Expression of disgust
68. Three, in Rome
69. MacGraw or Larter

CROSSWORD 53

Across

1. Connecting words
5. Between
9. Where Ivory floats
13. Clothing ensemble
14. Portals
16. Skipper's direction
17. Thomas __ Edison
18. Dwelling
19. Mechanical repetition
20. Designers
22. Concurred
24. Risk
25. "Peter Pan" pirate
26. Grate harshly
29. Scallion's cousin
32. Midwest airport
33. Maned felines
34. Omaha's state (abbr.)
36. Adolescent outcast
37. Food scrap
38. Not there
39. Mild exclamation
40. Holding devices
42. Contract
43. Arranged, as feathers
45. Bingo "announcer"
46. NYC's NL team
47. NBA's Jason
48. Get free
51. Weights used as ballast
55. Hawaiian island
56. "The Hunchback of __ Dame"
58. Farm division
59. Ponder
60. Imaginary vision
61. Fashionably dressed
62. Heights (abbr.)
63. "Thin Man" canine
64. Withheld

Down

1. "Stat!"
2. Void
3. Opera songstress
4. Kind of transmission
5. Hold fast
6. Mary Tyler __
7. Promissory notes
8. "Grey's Anatomy" chars.
9. Large cask
10. Burn-soothing plant
11. Head (Fr.)
12. Listen
15. Sailor
21. Neck region
23. Congeals

25. Inoculations
26. Nightingale's gift
27. Bird sound
28. Less charred
29. Fathered
30. Sun Shaquille
31. To the point
33. Mislays
35. Six-pack brew
38. Restrained (2 wds.)
40. Biden, informally
41. Propose
42. Actress Diane

44. Web letters (hyph.)
45. Motion pictures
47. Gold measurement
48. Mme. Bovary
49. King of Israel
50. Religious group
51. Fr. female saints
52. Muscular pain
53. Hold firmly
54. Religious denomination
57. "Are you a man __ mouse?" (2 wds.)

CROSSWORD 54

Across

1. Supermodel Banks
5. Use a bike
10. "The Egg __" (2 wds.)
14. Disapproving sounds
15. Unaccompanied
16. Enjoy a book
17. __ pump
18. River mouth
19. Filly feature
20. Put up jam
22. Ogles
24. "Earl" star Jason
25. Actor Everett
26. Cindy Crawford, e.g.
30. The Cowboys' league (abbr.)
32. Like delicate openwork
35. Verdi works
37. Social class
39. __ and haw
41. Native metals
42. Dishonor
44. Italian city
45. Driveway sealer
46. Smile joyfully
47. Breakfast choice
49. Make well
51. Hawaiian necklace
53. Dubliners
54. Sword fight
56. Bert Bobbsey's twin
58. Tel Aviv's land
61. Naval commanders
66. Poultry pen
67. "Sound of Music" role
69. Sad news item, for short
70. Bloke from Bath
71. Sevareid and Ambler
72. Musician's audition tape
73. Tormé and Brooks
74. Takes five
75. Tread

Down

1. Cooking measurement (abbr.)
2. "Paint __ Wagon"
3. Caesar's city
4. Venomous snakes
5. Juan's father
6. Gridiron team
7. Pineapple brand
8. Busy insect
9. Dog walker's need
10. Fleet of armed ships
11. Within shouting distance
12. Copenhagen native
13. Bad day for Caesar
21. Jazz singer Fitzgerald
23. Communicate
25. __ up (stay silent)
26. Debatable

27. Humanitarian Winfrey
28. Plow pioneer
29. Sounds of uncertainty
31. Picture enclosure
33. Tex-Mex favorite
34. Positive answers
36. NNW's opposite
38. Modern (prefix)
40. Trig or calculus
43. School lockers locale
44. __ capita
46. Sapphire's color

48. Immodest skirt
50. Makes fit
52. Charge formally
55. "__ Gantry"
57. Accumulate
58. Missile initials
59. Needing liniment
60. Muddle
61. Onassis et al.
62. Fishing gear
63. Help
64. Small citrus fruit
65. Street sign
68. Common verb

CROSSWORD 55

Across

1. Clean thoroughly
6. Desk light
10. Cardinals' boss
14. Byword
15. Toast topper
16. Evading army duty (abbr.)
17. Group of eight musicians
18. Light beds
19. Idiot
20. Hired hoodlum
21. Lab rodent
22. Barters
24. Fasten securely
26. Hormel's canned concoction
27. Composer Berlin
30. A cow has four
34. Coward et al.
35. House plant
36. Derby, e.g.
37. Church sisters
38. Paper cup brand
39. 1958 Leslie Caron movie
40. Sense of self
41. Cry softly
42. Avis, to Hertz
43. Refashions a house
46. Secret

47. Fuse
48. "The __ of the Ancient Mariner"
49. Of the backbone
52. Teachers' gp.
53. Vessels like Noah's
57. Measured step
58. "Terrible" czar
60. Hogs
61. Completed
62. Grace __
63. Lustrous fabric
64. Danson and Mack
65. Lightning bug's output
66. Actress Jane

Down

1. City's haze
2. Designer Chanel
3. Sarge's pooch
4. Knives and forks
5. Go bad
6. "__ Hero"
7. Good many (2 wds.)
8. Came across
9. Defer
10. "The __ Game"
11. Had bills
12. Study closely
13. Caribous' cousins
21. Scrap
23. Dodge truck model
25. Naval officer (abbr.)
26. Undress

27. __ circle
28. "Moulin __!"
29. Fang injection
30. Male and female
31. Onionlike plant
32. "__ the Horrible"
33. Avocet's kin
35. Meadow
38. Abode
39. Reveal (2 wds.)
42. CD-__
44. Proprietors
45. Narc's org.

46. U.S. spy org.
48. Resubscribe
49. Tie blemish
50. Apply asphalt
51. Chilled
52. Western treaty org.
54. Pinup Hayworth
55. Make a sweater
56. Shipped
59. Part of an encyclopedia set (abbr.)
60. Compass pt.

CROSSWORD 56

Across

1. Son of Noah
5. Resist
9. Ways to get there (abbr.)
13. Unclothed
14. Not as common
16. Popular Nabisco cookie
17. Professional groups (abbr.)
18. Stood
19. __ McNally
20. Consecrating
22. Lariats
24. __ Christian Andersen
25. "Jane __" (Brontë book)
26. Analyzes ore
29. Two-wheeler
33. River ducks
34. Jaworski and Spinks
36. Judge's title (abbr.)
37. Cash drawer
38. Performing
39. Small arrow
40. "I Like __"
41. Garden flower
42. Singer Frankie
43. Backyard heap's contents
45. Tarter
46. Roberto's rahs
47. Bit of kindling
48. Salt holder
51. First year student
55. Jeans name
56. Cherish
58. Filled tortilla
59. Lena or Ken
60. Official command
61. Reverberate
62. Apartment house, e.g. (abbr.)
63. French holy women (abbr.)
64. Stink

Down

1. Snooty person
2. Throw
3. Margin
4. GI's restaurant (2 wds.)
5. Lets out water from a sink
6. Receives wages
7. Toadlike creature
8. "Absolutely!"
9. Bandleader Jimmy __
10. Gershwin and Levin
11. TV's "__ 911!"
12. Pieces of turf
15. Depending (on)
21. Vocalizes
23. Circle parts
25. Keyboard wood

26. Storage spot
27. Watchmaker
28. Massachusetts city
30. Seat
31. Actor Greene
32. Penetrate
34. Plunders
35. Bonn "one"
38. Be entitled to
39. Carrie Fisher, to Debbie Reynolds
41. Athlete's vaulting need
42. Superman's sweetheart
44. __ around (being nosy)
45. Candies
47. Cease-fire
48. Messy fellow
49. Satan's domain
50. Greedy
51. Move erratically
52. Disabling spray
53. Pang
54. Niche
57. Magazine clutter

CROSSWORD 57

Across

1. Memo letters
5. Ebenezer Scrooge, for one
10. Took the subway
14. Dove coop
15. Undo laces
16. "__ the Rainbow"
17. Gravy no-no
18. Slides on ice
19. Indonesian island
20. Overturns
22. People's __ of China
24. Game official, informally
26. By __ (from memory)
27. Closing numbers
31. Walk the straight and __
35. Comic Youngman
36. Cardiff natives
38. Physicians' gp.
39. Once again
40. Aladdin's helper
41. Norse god
42. Decorate a cake
43. Pigeons, e.g.
44. Shade of blue
45. Cash in coupons
47. Diane and Tom
49. Charitable gift
51. Offense
52. Stretchable fabrics
56. Niece's counterpart
61. Caron film
62. Fusspot
64. Top-drawer (2 wds.)
65. Jib, e.g.
66. Holmes of "Dawson's Creek"
67. Boxed chart
68. Bohemian
69. Pay out
70. Finishes

Down

1. Bill of Rights defenders (abbr.)
2. Chicken noodle, e.g.
3. Bank machines (abbr.)
4. "__ Le Moko"
5. Mollusk
6. Pen fluid
7. Agitate
8. Downy duck
9. Reply
10. Highwayman
11. The __ Office
12. Lox location
13. Children's author Carle
21. Waiter's equipment
23. Arizona's neighbor
25. Smaller in number
27. Yard divider

28. "Baby __ Your Loving" (2 wds.)
29. Wind dir.
30. Posts a letter
32. "M*A*S*H" role
33. Overlooks
34. Lessen
35. Kojak's lack
37. Bonet, Simpson, and Hartman
40. Tricks
41. Juan's cheer
43. Sash

44. "Auld Lang __"
46. With little effort
48. Batted an eye
50. __ metal
52. Columnist Maxwell
53. Untruthful one
54. Deplaned
55. Satisfy
57. Senate gofer
58. __ of plenty
59. Author Bagnold
60. Marries
63. Author Anaïs __

CROSSWORD 58

Across

1. Papa's partner
5. "__ Suite"
10. Dundee resident
14. Juan's cheers
15. Age
16. Green bean
17. Rowing needs
18. Fed the kitty
19. Toaster __
20. Reveal
22. Nursing a drink
24. Circular
26. Fixes a squeak
27. Assert
30. Lots of times
33. Cola company
34. Gaze amorously
35. Sickness carrier
39. Dover's locale (abbr.)
40. Direct an orchestra
43. __ chi (martial art)
44. Turnpike
46. Gently persuade
47. Pressing tools
49. Famed cowboy star
51. Tilts downward
52. Chair part
54. Brogans
56. Plain-weave cotton cloth
59. Aviator Amelia
63. Villainous
64. Pat of "Wheel of Fortune" fame
66. Jacob's brother
67. "__ the Great" (kids' books)
68. Show conclusively
69. Film locales
70. Taverns' stock
71. Knight's horse
72. Assigned work

Down

1. It could be good or bad
2. Jai __
3. Game show tycoon Griffin
4. Guarantees
5. Capital on the Vltava River
6. Flax cloth
7. Likely (to)
8. 26th letters
9. "The King __" (2 wds.)
10. Slanting
11. __ War
12. Forewarnings
13. Zest
21. Valid thinking
23. "The Raven" poet
25. Hot time (2 wds.)
27. Impersonator
28. Comedian Jay
29. Inits. for Lopez

31. Continuous change
32. Detective, informally
34. __ about (approximately, 2 wds.)
36. English school
37. Rave
38. __ Marple of mysteries
41. Pumpkin mo.
42. Expert with mosaics
45. Hangs
48. Most foolhardy

50. "Gross!"
51. Drenched
52. Opponent
53. Join forces
55. Haul up
56. Rowlands of film
57. Poisonous snakes
58. Marketplace
60. On a voyage
61. Snitches
62. Walrus's tooth
65. Footballer Namath

PUZZLE 1

PUZZLE 2

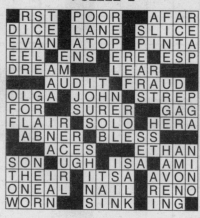

PUZZLE 3

PUZZLE 4

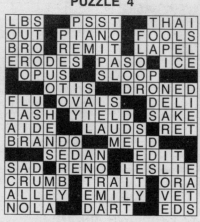

PUZZLE 5

PUZZLE 6

PUZZLE 7

```
INNS   GLEE    BMW
COOL  ALUMNI   EEE
YODA  CARUSO   LAB
 NETWORK    WALLS
    ARES   DAN
GOVERN    SENTRY
ALIAS  DIMES   OAF
MITT  PIOUS   BALE
EVA  ALONG   MARIE
 ELINOR    MORSEL
   NED   CHIP
ISLAM    RINSING
ROI   INTAKE  SOUR
OSS   ANSWER  ALSO
NAT   WELD    WATT
```

PUZZLE 8

```
FAB  AFT   GEL   AFB
ONA  DOE   AGE   LIE
ATL  DOM   BOO   LET
LIMA  LPS      SEALS
   CUSTOMS    ANDY
CHOMP     DICES
EATERS    AMATEUR
ORT  OCT   INC   SAT
 MOTORED   THINGS
   STARE     ERASE
ALDA   PICASSO
ROARS    KIA   NEED
ISM   EYE   DUD   ALE
SEE   MET   ETO   RIM
ESS   ISA   DES   NEO
```

PUZZLE 9

```
AGT   CLEAT   TINS
PURR  RIODE   INFO
ELIE  INNER   MALT
 FOCUSES   MAI
   ESPN   KINDER
ABODE  SANTA  LEW
DINES   DIET   EGO
AGED   JOT    AVER
MTA  OMAR    OPENS
SOL  SONNY   MONTE
 PSALMS   ASIS
   POE   SWATTER
SPAR  NOUNS   LAOS
HEMI  TALES   ERIK
HAIL  STUDY   PLY
```

PUZZLE 10

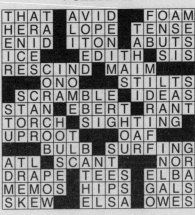

```
THAT  AVID    FOAM
HERA  LOPE   TENSE
ENID  ITON   ABUTS
ICE    EDITH   SIS
RESCIND   MAIM
   ONO    STILTS
 SCRAMBLE  IDEAS
STAN  EBERT   RANT
TORCH  SIGHTING
UPROOT    OAF
  BULB   SURFING
ATL  SCANT    NOR
DRAPE  TEES   ELBA
MEMOS  HIPS   GALS
SKEW   ELSA   OWES
```

PUZZLE 11

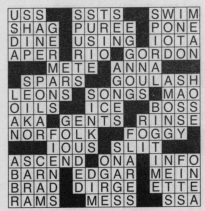

```
USS   SSTS    SWIM
SHAG  PUREE   PONE
DINE  USING   IOTA
APER  RIO    GORDON
   METE   ANNA
 SPARS    GOULASH
LEONS  SONGS  MAO
OILS   ICE    BOSS
AKA   GENTS   RINSE
NORFOLK    FOGGY
  IOUS    SLIT
ASCEND  ONA   INFO
BARN  EDGAR   MEIN
BRAD  DIRGE   ETTE
RAMS  MESS    SSA
```

PUZZLE 12

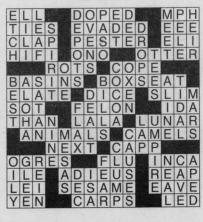

```
ELL   DOPED   MPH
TIES  EVADED  EEE
CLAP  PESTER  ELI
HIFI  ONO    OTTER
   ROTS   COPE
BASINS   BOXSEAT
ELATE  DICE   SLIM
SOT   FELON   IDA
THAN  LALA   LUNAR
 ANIMALS   CAMELS
   NEXT   CAPP
OGRES   FLU   INCA
ILE   ADIEUS  REAP
LEI   SESAME  EAVE
YEN   CARPS   LED
```

PUZZLE 13

```
M T V _ M A S T _ S L I T
O W E N O B E Y S _ N I C E
R I T A _ T I A R A _ O V E N
K N O B _ E D N A S _ R E D D
_ _ I D L E S _ H E E _ _ _
_ J E S U S _ _ B E T R A Y S
T E A C H _ A M I S S _ R U E
H E R O _ M L B _ _ P O K E
A R T _ N O O K S _ A R M O R
T S H I R T S _ _ O C E A N _
_ _ R A H _ H I R E S _ _ _
G Y R O _ E M E N D _ U M P S
L O A N _ R O L L E _ M O A T
O D I E _ S O L A R _ E N V Y
B A L D _ S O W S _ T E X _
```

PUZZLE 14

```
C O E D _ E V E N _ O C H O
S W O R D _ L I T E _ W R A P
A N N I E _ M E R V _ L U B E
_ _ _ F A R _ S E A M _ M I N
B O O T L E G _ _ D O U B T
I B M S _ A L F _ A S H _ _
N E A _ L O L A _ T O R C H
G Y R O _ M A Y B E _ H A H A
E S S A Y _ T E L L _ V A N
_ _ H A D _ R E V _ P E L E
_ A Z U R E _ _ R E M A R K S
I V E _ N E C K _ S O T _ _
R E S T _ P O N G _ L I M E S
A R T E _ E L E E _ L O R N E
S T Y X _ N E E D _ S I D E
```

PUZZLE 15

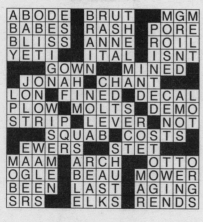

```
A B O D E _ B R U T _ M G M
B A B E S _ R A S H _ P O R E
B L I S S _ A N N E _ R O I L
Y E T I _ I T A L _ I S N T
_ _ G O W N _ M I N E D _ _
_ J O N A H _ C H A N T _ _
L O N _ F I N E D _ D E C A L
P L O W _ M O L T S _ D E M O
S T R I P _ L E V E R _ N O T
_ _ S Q U A B _ C O S T S _
_ E W E R S _ S T E T _ _ _
M A A M _ A R C H _ O T T O
O G L E _ B E A U _ M O W E R
B E E N _ L A S T _ A G I N G
S R S _ E L K S _ R E N D S
```

PUZZLE 16

```
M E L T _ S A N _ S I L K
A R E A S _ T I R E _ T R I O
S O N J A _ E D A M _ R O M P
H S T _ C R E E _ P H O N E S
_ _ S H I P _ L I E D _ _ _
S T A K E D _ _ A R R E S T
A U D I T S _ T O E D _ P H D
P L O D _ B B S _ _ D O R A
S I B _ A Q U A _ G R O C E R
P E A N U T _ _ R A C K E T
_ _ S N I T _ M I N K _ _ _
L E S S E N _ D I N G _ R P M
A C L U _ C O I L _ E N O L A
W H I M _ Y A R N _ S E D A N
N O P E _ F E E _ B E N S
```

PUZZLE 17

```
A T L _ S A A B _ D U P E
C H A W _ A L V I N _ E T A L
H A I R _ V O I L A _ B A L K
E T R E _ I N D _ B R A H M S
_ _ C L O G _ A B E S _ _ _
B E A K E R _ _ S E V E N S
R I D E S _ R E I D _ A L E
O D O R S _ E D D _ P R I E D
W E B _ R A T E _ R A V E N
_ R E S T E D _ T O P E K A
_ _ P A T S _ P O M P _ _ _
H U M A N E _ L I L _ E L L S
U S E D _ S H A P E _ R O I L
E D I E _ T I L E D _ S O F A
S A N D _ T A R O _ N E W _
```

PUZZLE 18

```
D M V _ W A F T _ S I C
M A U I _ C E L L O _ O N L Y
A L T O _ A D I O S _ M O O D
E Y E L I D _ S U S P E N D S
_ _ _ I N D _ T R E A T _ _
_ P E N C I L _ _ S L I C E
A L L _ H E A R D _ S M I L E
V O T E _ D Y E R S _ E V E R
A T O M S _ S P O T S _ I V E
S N E E R _ _ P I C K L E _
_ _ R E A C H _ R A N _ _ _
P R E A M B L E _ F R E E Z E
B A W L _ B A R E R _ E X A M
S H E D _ I R O N Y _ L I P S
_ S R S _ S A N G _ S T S _
```

PUZZLE 19

```
A B C . A I L S . U S S R
F L U B . S M E E . S H E E T
T U B A . K I N D . M I N E O
. R E D D E N . A L A M O D E
. . E R R . S K I . M R S .
P I G G Y . E L A P S E . .
O L E G . F O Y . T O R S O S
S S N . R O N . C O T . A P E
H A T B O X . I A N . F L I T
. . E D I S O N . S I T E S
. M A E . E A U . S U N . .
R O L L E R S . S T E I N S .
A V O I D . H A I R . T A I L
H E N N A . A B L E . E G G O
. S E E M . Y E L P . S H Y .
```

PUZZLE 20

```
W I S C . R B I S . . A S S
O A T H . N E I G H . B L O T
K N E E . A T A L E . A L D A
. S P R A T . S O L . L I S T
. . U H U H . O V A L . .
B A R B A R A . E N A C T S
A M Y S . A V I V . A D O R E
N O D . C L O S E S T . V I N
G R E T A . C A R P . D E B S
S E R E N A . N O M I N E E
. . R E V S . E K E S . .
S T I R . A M I . A L P H A
O H N O . T I T A N . L A W S
H E I R . A T O N E . A L O E
O N T . R E N T . Y E L P
```

PUZZLE 21

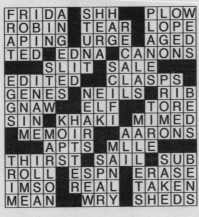

```
F R I D A . S H H . P L O W
R O B I N . T E A R . L O P E
A P I N G . U R G E . A G E D
T E D . E D N A . C A N O N S
. . S L I T . S A L E . .
E D I T E D . C L A S P S
G E N E S . N E I L S . R I B
G N A W . E L F . T O R E
S I N . K H A K I . M I M E D
. M E M O I R . A A R O N S
. . A P T S . M L L E . .
T H I R S T . S A I L . S U B
R O L L . E S P N . E R A S E
I M S O . R E A L . T A K E N
M E A N . W R Y . S H E D S
```

PUZZLE 22

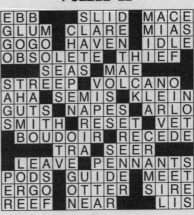

```
E B B . S L I D . M A C E
G L U M . C L A R E . M I A S
G O G O . H A V E N . I D L E
O B S O L E T E . T H I E F
. . S E A S . M A E . .
S T R E E P . V O L C A N O
A H A . S E M I S . K L E I N
G U T S . N A P E S . A R L O
S M I T H . R E S E T . V E T
B O U D O I R . R E C E D E
. . T R A . S E E R . .
L E A V E . P E N N A N T S
P O D S . G U I D E . M E E T
E R G O . O T T E R . S I R E
R E E F . N E A R . L I S
```

PUZZLE 23

```
A M I . W H O A . P A T S
L E O S . S E A R S . E V I L
P A N T . L I L T S . N I N A
S T E A L E R S . M A D A M
. . T O E D . G I R L . .
W A K E U P . M A N I T O B A
A L A N . S T O R K . Y A R D
N O R . R O B . S I D
T H E E . J A C O B . T I D E
S A N D W I C H . R A I S E D
. . W A G E . T O G A . .
R A D A R . M O N O R A I L
O N O R . A G E N T . A L S O
M E L D . K A T I E . S L I P
A W L S . A L E C . I N S
```

PUZZLE 24

```
A V I S . M B A . R O M A
M I M I C . Y O G I . E X E S
F L A S H . R Y A N . G E E K
M E N . O A R S . S T I N K S
. . H I G H . S O H O . .
S P H E R E . C A L E N D A R
K E Y S . S T A L E . S I R E
I T E . I R E . A S A
M A N S . H E L M S . O N O R
P L A T E A U S . E L L E N S
. . R S V P . D E E D . .
T O Y O T A . C O R A . S P A
O P A L . N E L L . P E C A N
T E L L . A N A T . S W O R N
O D E S . D D S . E T T E
```

PUZZLE 25

```
MAIM   TWAS   OMAR
ASTI  OHARE   PILE
PIER  CEDED   ACED
 AMIGO  ENABLES
   ARNE   AKA
STAMINA   ARCTIC
ARR NOTES  BURRO
NAME RURAL  BEAU
TIEUP PETAL  ATL
ANDREW   ABETTED
   RAH  NEVE
 MISTIER  LIARS
HALO SLIDE  SALE
USSR TEPID  ETON
THAT  SNAG  SEWS
```

PUZZLE 26

```
ANNA   PREP   SAG
MOOT  DIANE  HIRT
FRET  YENTA  ODIE
MALIGN  GENERATE
   LOA  ERUPT
 PSALMS   TEALS
ELK DOILY  EGYPT
LAIR SNOOT  ERIE
STEEL SODAS  IND
 EDDIE   ANTICS
   BARBS  NUN
SYCAMORE  ENSUES
SEAR DIVAS  INTO
TARO EBERT  STOW
HEN  DENT  TONS
```

PUZZLE 27

```
SLAB   ACT   DELL
CAROL  BRIC  EDIE
AMIGO  NEER  BEEN
MEA SKEW  URANUS
   PEER  PIES
 STERN  ROSIEST
BARNS SHRED  HIT
ONAN LAYER  FORE
ATM HELMS  BLEED
 APPEASE  ALOSS
   ANNA  SNAP
AVERSE  KIDD  EDT
WALT RANG  ERNIE
LIKE SLIM  SEVEN
SLED   STA  GYMS
```

PUZZLE 28

```
THEM   ACT   EVES
RELIC  ROVE  LIAM
IRISH  COAL  ECRU
 RETIRES  ACCEPT
   LID  JILT
SALADS WANE  ASP
OLIN ELOPER  SAO
RINSE IMA  KINGS
END RECANT  VEES
SEA RAIN  AVERSE
   LEST  EKE
DECODE  BLENDED
IRAS USER  OOZES
MLLE POLO  MORAL
EELS  BAY  MANY
```

PUZZLE 29

```
BEEP   SEN   GOAL
ALVA  LILAC  ROPE
LIEU  ARMOR  EZRA
MALLET  SMUDGES
   ALEC  IND
ARC BRAT  CEASED
GOLDA NOAH  BARA
ABEE SORRY  LIAR
VIAL HEAR  DENSE
ENTICE HOPI  TED
   ORT  WREN
 SESSION  EMOTED
LODE FLOSS  RIDE
BONE FLEAS  TRAM
STAN  SST  HEMI
```

PUZZLE 30

```
ASPS   ASIA   AHAB
BORE  CHORE   BALI
CHAPERONES   UNIT
DOM VEES   CBS
   PASS  TALENT
GMEN  TAPE   ARC
MOONS SHIED  BIO
BARN SCENE  ABBR
ADE ROOST  CREED
SEN IDLE   LIDS
 DOODAD  LAYS
   PEP BOND  LOO
RITA  ORANGEBOWL
POOL PANEL  ELEE
MUMS  HERE  DANS
```

PUZZLE 31

```
WHIZ  LILAC  ▮ FBI
NATO  AMILE  REED
BRED  CAROL  EARL
ADMIRE  AOL  ARTY
▮ AIRS  FOOD ▮
RECLASP  SLIME
AHA  ETTA  DEALT
RITA  ESSEN  DREW
KNELT  TAUT  DNA
ONION  ASTORIA
GOES  ERGO
BEAN  SHH  IODINE
MLLE  TEASE  NOEL
WILD  LATIN  ETAL
SAY  ERECT  YAPS
```

PUZZLE 32

```
ROAM  AAA  USED
EDGES  USMA  NOPE
BOONE  DIAZ  CREE
ARG  RHEA  ASLEEP
IVAN  ALTO
BOATED  NEIGHS
AILED  CIGAR  ETE
SLAM  RILES  PIER
HEM  PETER  ORDER
DOSAGE  AVOIDS
LAUD  CHEW
RECURL  LIAR  OSS
EDAM  ARID  DITTO
LISP  RITE  ONION
YEAS  GER  ASPS
```

PUZZLE 33

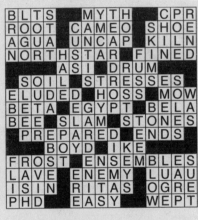

```
BLTS  MYTH  CPR
ROOT  CAMEO  SHOE
AGUA  UNCAP  KILN
NORTHSTAR  FINED
ASI  DRUM
SOIL  STRESSES
ELUDED  HOSS  MOW
BETA  EGYPT  BELA
BEE  SLAM  STONES
PREPARED  ENDS
BOYD  IKE
FROST  ENSEMBLES
LAVE  ENEMY  LUAU
ISIN  RITAS  OGRE
PHD  EASY  WEPT
```

PUZZLE 34

```
CALF  OSS  MEMO
ARIA  INKED  ISIN
REAL  SUITE  LANE
PARLORS  UNPLUGS
ERA  SPIRE
MANGERS  MERMAN
COW  ALINE  SOME
NRA  NIB  ADS  WES
BARB  SHREW  ENS
CLERIC  ALMONDS
ISLAM  ORA
CURTAIL  STERNUM
OPEN  PLUME  RONA
RODE  SIRED  OMIT
ANDY  NNE  WETS
```

PUZZLE 35

```
RAM  ACTOR  EGGS
AMIS  BLAME  NEMO
PETA  HANES  ANEW
TRENTON  NEWMANS
DIRGE  TAE
EARL  SSN  GLAD
INMATE  SHH  SCOW
STU  SST  LEG  HOE
MESH  PIG  MAKERS
REAL  PEW  BEDS
RIG  MAJOR
PROVERB  TURNSIN
EAVE  ARCED  ELMO
EVES  DAIRY  LOSS
LENT  STAYS  WOE
```

PUZZLE 36

```
DAVID  SATS  RIM
IMAGE  PTAS  TATA
VISOR  IBET  IFSO
ADE  BARA  SUB
PILOTS  REST
ASLEEP  TENTPEG
UNITS  TAILS  HAL
NONE  BUSES  PEPE
TOE  MILKS  AARON
SPUMONI  INSETS
SPAR  PANDAS
SKI  GEAR  CUB
PINK  MMII  CHASE
ACES  POLL  HORSE
RYE  SEES  YEARN
```

PUZZLE 37

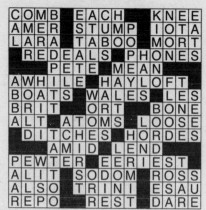

```
C O M B   E A C H     K N E E
A M E R   S T U M P   I O T A
L A R A   T A B O O   M O R T
  R E D E A L S   P H O N E S
      P E T E   M E A N
A W H I L E   H A Y L O F T
B O A T S   W A L E S   L E S
B R I T   O R T     B O N E
A L T   A T O M S   L O O S E
  D I T C H E S   H O R D E S
      A M I D   L E N D
P E W T E R   E E R I E S T
A L I T   S O D O M   R O S S
A L S O   T R I N I   E S A U
R E P O   R E S T   D A R E
```

PUZZLE 38

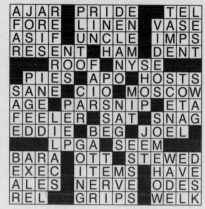

```
A J A R   P R I D E     T E L
F O R E   L I N E N   V A S E
A S I F   U N C L E   I M P S
R E S E N T   H A M   D E N T
      R O O F   N Y S E
  P I E S   A P O   H O S T S
S A N E   C I O   M O S C O W
A G E   P A R S N I P   E T A
F E E L E R   S A T   S N A G
E D D I E   B E G   J O E L
    L P G A   S E E M
B A R A   O T T   S T E W E D
E X E C   I T E M S   H A V E
A L E S   N E R V E   O D E S
R E L   G R I P S   W E L K
```

PUZZLE 39

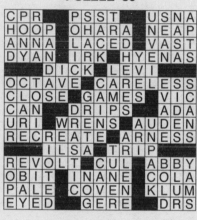

```
C P R   P S S T   U S N A
H O O P   O H A R A   N E A P
A N N A   L A C E D   V A S T
D Y A N   I R K   H Y E N A S
      D I C K   L E V I
O C T A V E   C A R E L E S S
C L O S E   G A M E S   V I C
C A N   D R I P S   A D A
U R I   W R E N S   A U D E N
R E C R E A T E   A R N E S S
    I L S A   T R I P
R E V O L T   C U L   A B B Y
O B I T   I N A N E   C O L A
P A L E   C O V E N   K L U M
E Y E D   G E R E   D R S
```

PUZZLE 40

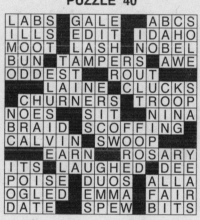

```
L A B S   G A L E   A B C S
I L L S   E D I T   I D A H O
M O O T   L A S H   N O B E L
B U N   T A M P E R S   A W E
O D D E S T   R O U T
    L A I N E   C L U C K S
  C H U R N E R S   T R O O P
N O E S   S I T   N I N A
B R A I D   S C O F F I N G
C A L V I N   S W O O P
    E A R N   R O S A R Y
I T S   L A U G H E D   D E E
P O I S E   D U O S   A L L A
O G L E D   E M M A   F A I R
D A T E   S P E W   B I T S
```

PUZZLE 41

```
C L A M   A I N T   B A C H
I O W A   B R I E F   A C H Y
T O O N   S O B E R   S L I D
E N L I V E N   N E P T U N E
    F I N S   E E E
A S P E C T   S I Z E   F A T
C H O S E   M A C E R   R B I
T I L T   I R E   M A A M
E E L   E D N A S   S U I T E
D R S   V I E S   T E L L E R
    H E N   M A L T
F E D O R A S   A T F I R S T
G R I N   H E A R T   P E A K
H I R E   S A B L E   L E N O
I N K S   L E A D   E L K S
```

PUZZLE 42

```
A M F M   W I M P S   W O O
L O L A   A D U L T   V I V A
T R O T   K A T I E   E R I K
S E E T H E   T A N   N E D S
      H A S H   N O N E
  F L E D   O C T   C E A S E
D R E W   M R I   D I R E C T
A I M   T I N G L E S   S A T
L A U R E N   A O L   H O N E
E R R O R   N R A   R E P S
    B I T E   N A S A
M A G I   R E V   S T R O P S
A L A N   E D I T H   S L O P
K I T S   E L S I E   A G U A
E T E   S E A M S   Y A R N
```

PUZZLE 43

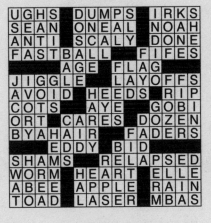

```
UGHS  DUMPS  IRKS
SEAN  ONEAL  NOAH
ANTI  SCALY  DONE
FASTBALL   FIFES
      AGE  FLAG
JIGGLE   LAYOFFS
AVOID  HEEDS  RIP
COTS   AYE   GOBI
ORT  CARES  DOZEN
BYAHAIR    FADERS
    EDDY  BID
SHAMS   RELAPSED
WORM  HEART  ELLE
ABEE  APPLE  RAIN
TOAD  LASER  MBAS
```

PUZZLE 44

```
ASH   DEBS   TIBET
BOAR  ELLE  ADLAI
BALE  MAAM  SLURS
APOLLOTHIRTEEN
   IONE    HES
SAFER  DUTY   ASP
CRAVE  NAME   GAL
IDREAMOFJEANNIE
FOE  LONI  GEENA
IRS  TATS  LISTS
    KAT   OLEG
BANDOFBROTHERS
ROMEO  RATA  EVIL
ICIER  ABED  DALI
PASSE  TEDS   NED
```

PUZZLE 45

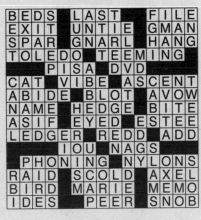

```
BEDS  LAST   FILE
EXIT  UNTIE  GMAN
SPAR  GNARL  HANG
TOLEDO   TEEMING
    PISA  DVD
CAT  VIBE  ASCENT
ABIDE  BLOT  AVOW
NAME  HEDGE  BITE
ASIF  EYED  ESTEE
LEDGER   REDD  ADD
     IOU  NAGS
PHONING   NYLONS
RAID  SCOLD  AXEL
BIRD  MARIE  MEMO
IDES   PEER  SNOB
```

PUZZLE 46

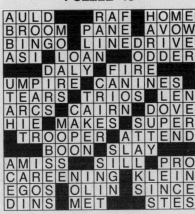

```
AULD   RAF   HOME
BROOM  PANE  AVOW
BINGO  LINEDRIVE
ASI  LOAN  ODDER
    DALY  FIRE
UMPIRE  CANINES
TEARS  TRIOS  LEN
ARCS  CAIRN  DOVE
HIE  MAKES  SUPER
TROOPER   ATTEND
    BOON  SLAY
AMISS  SILL   PRO
CAREENING  KLEIN
EGOS  OLIN  SINCE
DINS   MET   STES
```

PUZZLE 47

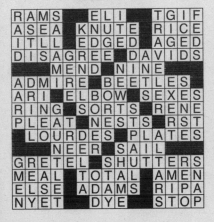

```
RAMS   ELI   TGIF
ASEA  KNUTE  RICE
ITLL  EDGED  AGED
DISAGREE   DAVIDS
    MEND  NINE
ADMIRE   BEETLES
ARI  ELBOW  SEXES
RING  SORTS  RENE
PLEAT  NESTS  RST
LOURDES   PLATES
    NEER  SAIL
GRETEL   SHUTTERS
MEAL  TOTAL  AMEN
ELSE  ADAMS  RIPA
NYET   DYE   STOP
```

PUZZLE 48

```
TWIN  CRUMB  BILL
VISA  LASER  OPIE
ALLS  OMEGA  NOLA
 TEACUPS   CANDID
      ADS  MERE
DRAWLS   POLITER
EASEL  BATES   RIB
MIST  EIGHT  TUNE
ONO  MUTES  LAPSE
 SCRAPER   CENTER
    UGHS   BOO
STUDIO   CEASING
TORE  RELAX  DELI
EGGS  IRENE  EVEN
POET  CROSS  SEED
```

PUZZLE 49

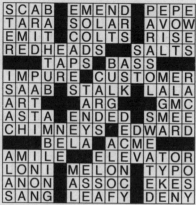

S	C	A	B		E	M	E	N	D		P	E	P	E
T	A	R	A		S	O	L	A	R		A	V	O	W
E	M	I	T		C	O	L	T	S		R	I	S	E
R	E	D	H	E	A	D	S			S	A	L	T	S
			T	A	P	S		B	A	S	S			
I	M	P	U	R	E		C	U	S	T	O	M	E	R
S	A	A	B		S	T	A	L	K		L	A	L	A
A	R	T				A	R	G				G	M	C
A	S	T	A		E	N	D	E	D		S	M	E	E
C	H	I	M	N	E	Y	S		E	D	W	A	R	D
			B	E	L	A		A	C	M	E			
A	M	I	L	E			E	L	E	V	A	T	O	R
L	O	N	I		M	E	L	O	N		T	Y	P	O
A	N	O	N		A	S	S	O	C		E	K	E	S
S	A	N	G		L	E	A	F	Y		D	E	N	Y

PUZZLE 50

A	M	I	D		A	S	K	S		G	A	Z	A
T	A	C	O		R	O	A	S	T		I	R	A	N
T	R	I	M		M	A	N	N	A		R	I	N	D
I	L	E		N	I	K	E		P	U	L	S	E
C	A	R	B	O	N	S		F	I	R	S	T
			A	U	G		B	O	N	N		O	W	N
A	C	O	R	N		F	L	A	G	S		T	I	E
S	U	V	S		S	E	A	M	S		A	L	L	A
I	R	E		A	L	A	N	S		S	L	E	E	P
F	D	R		L	A	R	K		P	H	D
		T	R	O	T	S		C	L	E	A	R	U	P
F	A	I	T	H		L	I	E	S		A	R	E
A	R	K	S		E	V	I	T	A		E	G	G	S
L	E	E	K		R	O	L	E	S		W	E	E	K
P	E	N	S		W	I	D	E		E	D	D	Y

PUZZLE 51

P	A	C	E		S	M	U	T		U	P	S	Y
E	A	R	L		C	U	R	S	E		T	I	M	E
T	R	O	D		E	D	S	E	L		E	X	E	S
A	P	P	E	A	R	S		R	L	S		I	L	E
			S	T	A	Y		I	N	S	E	T	S
C	U	S	T	O	M		S	I	T	U	P
O	T	T		M	I	D	A	S		B	O	W	L	S
W	A	I	F		C	E	L	E	B		T	A	I	L
S	H	R	U	G		S	T	E	E	P		N	E	A
			S	E	M	I	S		T	I	E	D	U	P
C	A	M	E	R	A		G	W	E	N
A	D	E		M	L	B		A	E	R	I	A	L	S
N	O	T	A		I	R	A	T	E		G	R	E	W
D	R	A	W		G	I	V	E	N		M	I	N	I
Y	E	L	L		N	E	E	D		A	D	A	M

PUZZLE 52

I	F	S	O		R	A	M	P	S		A	C	R	E
L	I	M	P		I	D	I	O	T		M	O	O	N
E	D	I	T		P	L	A	T	E		B	R	A	D
S	E	T		J	A	I		I	D	L	E	R	S
	L	E	N	O		B	E	R	N	I	E
		C	H	A	S	T	E		E	D	G	E	D
B	E	G	I	N	S		A	B	C	S		A	Y	E
A	L	M	S		H	A	G	A	R		W	I	R	E
N	E	A		H	E	R	E		E	M	I	N	E	M
G	E	N	O	A		C	R	U	E	T	S
		C	H	O	S	E	N		N	E	E	R
N	A	S	C	A	R		I	N	S		L	A	M
A	C	L	U		N	U	T	T	Y		A	L	V	A
T	I	E	R		O	G	R	E	S		L	I	E	N
O	D	D	S		T	H	E	S	E		I	S	L	E

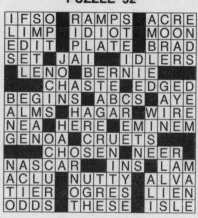

PUZZLE 53

A	N	D	S		A	M	I	D		B	A	T	H
S	U	I	T		D	O	O	R	S		A	L	E	E
A	L	V	A		H	O	U	S	E		R	O	T	E
P	L	A	N	N	E	R	S		A	G	R	E	E	D
			D	A	R	E		S	M	E	E
S	C	R	A	P	E		S	H	A	L	L	O	T
O	H	A	R	E		L	I	O	N	S		N	E	B
N	E	R	D		O	R	T			H	E	R	E
G	E	E		V	I	S	E	S		L	E	A	S	E
		P	R	E	E	N	E	D		C	A	L	L	E	R
			M	E	T	S		K	I	D	D
E	S	C	A	P	E		S	A	N	D	B	A	G	S
M	A	U	I		N	O	T	R	E		A	C	R	E
M	U	L	L		D	R	E	A	M		C	H	I	C
A	L	T	S			A	S	T	A		K	E	P	T

PUZZLE 54

T	Y	R	A		P	E	D	A	L		A	N	D	I
B	O	O	S		A	L	O	N	E		R	E	A	D
S	U	M	P		D	E	L	T	A		M	A	N	E
P	R	E	S	E	R	V	E		S	T	A	R	E	S
			L	E	E		C	H	A	D
M	O	D	E	L		N	F	L		L	A	C	Y
O	P	E	R	A	S		R	A	N	K		H	E	M
O	R	E	S		S	H	A	M	E		P	I	S	A
T	A	R		B	E	A	M		O	M	E	L	E	T
	H	E	A	L		L	E	I		I	R	I	S	H
			D	U	E	L		N	A	N
I	S	R	A	E	L		A	D	M	I	R	A	L	S
C	O	O	P		M	A	R	I	A		O	B	I	T
B	R	I	T		E	R	I	C	S		D	E	M	O
M	E	L	S		R	E	S	T	S		S	T	E	P

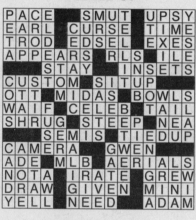

PUZZLE 55

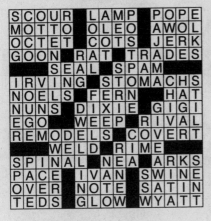

```
S C O U R   L A M P   P O P E
M O T T O   O L E O   A W O L
O C T E T   C O T S   J E R K
G O O N   R A T   T R A D E S
      S E A L   S P A M
I R V I N G   S T O M A C H S
N O E L S   F E R N   H A T
N U N S   D I X I E   G I G I
E G O   W E E P   R I V A L
R E M O D E L S   C O V E R T
      W E L D   R I M E
S P I N A L   N E A   A R K S
P A C E   I V A N   S W I N E
O V E R   N O T E   S A T I N
T E D S   G L O W   W Y A T T
```

PUZZLE 56

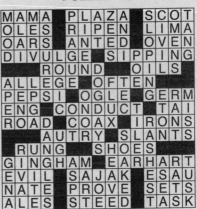

```
S H E M   D E F Y   D I R S
N U D E   R A R E R   O R E O
O R G S   A R O S E   R A N D
B L E S S I N G   L A S S O S
        H A N S   E Y R E
A S S A Y S   B I C Y C L E
T E A L S   L E O N S   H O N
T I L L   D O I N G   D A R T
I K E   P E O N Y   L A I N E
C O M P O S T   S O U R E R
      O L E S   T W I G
S H A K E R   F R E S H M A N
L E V I   V A L U E   T A C O
O L I N   E D I C T   E C H O
B L D G   S T E S   R E E K
```

PUZZLE 57

```
A S A P   M I S E R   R O D E
C O T E   U N T I E   O V E R
L U M P   S K I D S   B A L I
U P S E T S   R E P U B L I C
      R E F   R O T E
  F I N A L E S   N A R R O W
H E N N Y   W E L S H   A M A
A N E W   G E N I E   O D I N
I C E   B I R D S   S L A T E
R E D E E M   S A W Y E R S
      A L M S   S I N
E L A S T I C S   N E P H E W
L I L I   C R A N K   A O N E
S A I L   K A T I E   G R I D
A R T Y   S P E N D   E N D S
```

PUZZLE 58

```
M A M A   P L A Z A   S C O T
O L E S   R I P E N   L I M A
O A R S   A N T E D   O V E N
D I V U L G E   S I P P I N G
      R O U N D   O I L S
A L L E G E   O F T E N
P E P S I   O G L E   G E R M
E N G   C O N D U C T   T A I
R O A D   C O A X   I R O N S
      A U T R Y   S L A N T S
      R U N G   S H O E S
G I N G H A M   E A R H A R T
E V I L   S A J A K   E S A U
N A T E   P R O V E   S E T S
A L E S   S T E E D   T A S K
```